Greavsie's
SPORTS QUIZ
CHALLENGE

2

Norman Giller

HAMLYN

To James Jnr and Alexander
They have all the answers

Acknowledgements

Norman Giller, devisor and compiler of Greavsie's Sports Quiz Challenge, wishes to thank Peter Arnold for his diligent editing, Piers Murray Hill and David Ballheimer for their motivating powers, Michael Giller for his Apple-a-day computer talent, artist David Edwards for his graphic suport, *The Sun* for allowing me to use their daily teaser, The Name Game, and—most of all—James Greaves for letting me keep him puzzled for hours on end. Greavsie's scored yet again!

Published by Paul Hamlyn Publishing
A division of the Octopus Group Limited
Michelin House, 81 Fulham Road
London SW3 6RB
and distributed for them by
Octopus Distribution Services Limited
Rushden, Northamptonshire, England

Typeset and designed
by Norman Giller Enterprises,
Shoeburyness, Essex, England

Front cover photograph by Nick Lockett/Central Television

First published in 1988
ISBN 0 600 55887 8

Printed in the Channel Islands by Guernsey Press Company Ltd.

Contents

	Maximum Score	Page

(Maximum score possible: 2,970 points)

Prepare yourself for the 'inquizition!'

By Jimmy Greaves

I must warn you that this book is dangerous. Once you pick it up you can't put it down—that's if you consider yourself anything of a sports fan. There is a challenge on every single page with hundreds of questions and teasers that will have you puzzling for hours on end. I have been put through the wringer by question compiler Norman Giller who checked off each of my answers like an examination inspector. He turned it into something of an 'inquizition!'

You will find my scores recorded on each page and my final total is registered at the back of the book on page 190, along with a Ratings Guide so that you can judge whether you are a sports mastermind or, like me, somebody with just a better than average all-round knowledge of sport.

Each page presents you with a two-pronged challenge. Your first target will be to beat the average score—assessed by testing an across-the-board mix of 100 sports fans of all ages. Then see if you can score better than me, and if you watch my performances as a resident captain on Central TV's *Sporting Triangles* you will know that it should not be too difficult!

You can keep a check on your score and your running total in the scorecheck boxes at the bottom of each page. The answers to each quiz are are at the foot of the next page but one, so you don't have to go searching around at the back of the book every few minutes to find out whether or not you are right.

I 'm sure you will enjoy the novel way in which the quizzes are presented. You can test your boxing knowledge in a world championship contest, go for a big score in a Test match special, try your all-round knowledge on the snooker table, aim for doubles and trebles on the darts board, take a trip round the Grand National course, see if you are switched-on with television sport, take on a computer in a ratings contest, go 18 holes in an Open golf quiz, and play the World Cup and FA Cup Final games.

We already know that this unique formula works because of the success of our first Sports Quiz Challenge book. If you were with us the first time round, thanks for again accepting our challenge. I think you will find this book even more challenging and entertaining than the first.

We are in knowledgeable company with quiz master Norman Giller. He is the man who devised ITV's argument-provoking series *Who's the Greatest?*, and he scripted the compelling Olympics documentary *The Games of '48* in tandem with his close friend Brian Moore. He is also the creator and compiler of *The Sun's* longest-running feature, *The Name Game*, and has at various times had more than 20 quiz and puzzle-game features published in national newspapers. This is our 12th book in harness together and he has had another 20 books published on sporting themes since switching to freelance work after ten years as a sportswriter on the *Daily Express*.

So all in all he has the ideal background to set the following quizzes that I am sure will provide you with hours of entertainment. You can turn it into a team game by trying the quizzes on your friends to see if they can beat you score.

It's a book that you *play* rather than read. I hope you enjoy taking the Sports Challenge. I promise you, it's a funny old game!

1 JUST FOR STARTERS

We start off with a warm-up test. Award yourself one point for each correct answer that is a surname starting with the same initial.
Average score: 6
Greavsie: 8

1. WHO was the first footballer capped 100 times by England?

2. WHO was the last British winner of an individual title in the lawn tennis championships at Wimbledon?

3. WHO is the snooker star nicknamed 'The Whirlwind'?

4. WHO was Britain's first post-war British heavyweight boxing champion? He took the title from Jack London.

5. WHO was the England international goalkeeper signed by Rangers from Norwich City?

6. WHO won the gold medal for Britain in the 200 metres breast-stroke in the 1976 Montreal Olympics?

7. WHO won the Suntory World Matchplay Golf championship in 1987?

8. WHO is the New Zealand athlete who became the first man to break the 3mins 50secs barrier in the mile?

9. WHO was the Scottish international footballer nicknamed 'The Ghost of White Hart Lane'?

10. WHO was the opening batsman who captained Lancashire and played in 37 Tests for England?

ANSWERS

The answers to each quiz will appear on the next page but one. Keep a check on your score as you go along and then compare your final total with the RATINGS GUIDE on pages 190-191.

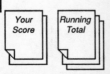

Your Score

Running Total

ODD ONE OUT

Who is the odd one out in each of the following six lists? We give you a little 'think hint' to help. Award yourself two points for each correct answer.
Average score: 6 Greavsie: 8

1. British boxers Mark Kaylor, Herol Graham, Randolph Turpin, Alan Minter, Kevin Finnegan, Maurice Hope, Roy Gumbs, Tony Sibson. *Think British middleweight titles.*

2. England footballers Gordon Banks, George Cohen, Norman Hunter, Ray Wilson, Nobby Stiles, Jack Charlton, Bobby Moore. *Think 1966 World Cup.*

3. Olympic medallists Ann Packer, Mary Peters, Mary Rand, Judy Grinham, Maureen Gardner, Tessa Sanderson, Anita Lonsborough. *Think gold medals.*

4. Test cricketers Geoff Boycott, John Edrich, Graham Gooch, Tom Graveney, Jack Hobbs, Herbert Sutcliffe, Len Hutton, Colin Milburn. *Think openers.*

5. National hunt jockeys Fred Winter, Bob Champion, Johnny Francome, Tommy Stack, Bryan Fletcher, Pat Taafe, Dick Saunders. *Think Nationals.*

6. Rugby stars J.P.R. Williams, Paul Thorburn, Andy Irvine, Don Clarke, Mike Gibson, Serge Blanco, Bob Hiller, Bob Scott. *Think full backs.*

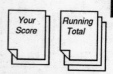

Your Score *Running Total*

ANSWERS

You will find the answers to this Odd One Out quiz on page 12.

3 SPORTSWORD

Award yourself two points for each clue that you solve plus a bonus of 18 points if you complete the crossword. **Average score: 32 Greavsie: 34**

ACROSS

1 One of the chosen full-backs in England's 1966 World Cup team (5).
7 Just multiply by two eights to name this annual event (4,4).
8 Fencers may try to do it in the lounge (5).
10 Queen is art for a skill on horseback (10).
12 Shouts from a 'keeper like Bonetti? (8).
14 For a start, David Bryant has had many of them on the bowls green (4).
16 Place it to aid a jockey, for instance (1,3).
17 Take just one turn out on a limb (5,3).
20 Bob Scott often did this in his bare feet for the All Blacks (6,4).
23 Mel and Seymour, who could always look after themselves (5).
24 Test ground in New Zealand that sounds a gardener's paradise? (4,4).
25 There is often a call for them before a ball is bowled (5).

DOWN

1 They are at home at Parkhead (6).
2 A nervous batting shot (4).
3 Pilgrims Park for away day teams! (4).
4 Playing condition in the USA? (5).
5 Races best watched from the grandstand? (9).
6 Perhaps a game to play in nets? (6).
9 The sequel to teams being like this is often a penalty shoot-out (5).
11 Exercises for team training at Dartmoor? (9)
13 He was like an eel in the goal area for Manchester City and England (3).
15 Sounds a pickpocket at the snooker table (5).
16 Forwards are not pleased when they are tapped (6).
18 There's only one Hubert but 18 of these (6).
19 Dickie, an England scrum-half who really drove his forwards (5).
21 Player of clubs (4).
22 Glue a toboggan? (4).

ANSWERS

Your Score | Running Total

4 THE TRIVIA TEST

See if you can select the right answer to each of these trivial sports questions. Award yourself two points for each correct answer.

Average score: 6   Greavsie: 8

1. Which Olympic champion threw his gold medal into a river in protest at being refused service in a whites-only restaurant?
a) Cassius Clay; b) Jesse Owens; c) Tommie Smith

2. Which Open golf championship runner-up missed winning because his ball became trapped in the neck of a broken bottle?
a) Dai Rees; b) Harry Bradshaw; c) Dave Thomas

3. Which former postman won the world snooker championship at his first attempt?
a) John Spencer; b) Terry Griffiths; c) Ray Reardon

4. Which Peruvian-born cricketer has captained England in post-war Test matches?
a) Ted Dexter; b) Mike Denness; c) Freddie Brown

5. Which former Scottish Rugby Union international owned 1979 Grand National winner Rubstic?
a) John Douglas; b) Ken Scotland; c) Ian McLauchlan

6. Which England fast bowler used to write poetry while sitting in the pavilion during matches?
a) Freddie Trueman; b) Fred Rumsey; c) John Snow

7. Which former Olympic champion earned more than $45 million dollars from a career in Hollywood?
a) Johnny Weissmuller; b) Sonja Henie; c) Bob Mathias

Your Score

Running Total

ANSWERS

HOW WELL D'YOU KNOW...?
BRYAN ROBSON

Award yourself one point for each question you can answer about Bryan Robson.
Average score: 5 Greavsie: 7

1. With which club did he start his Football League career?

2. Who was the manager who said in 1981: "He leaves this club over my dead body!"?

3. What was the fee when he joined Manchester United in October, 1981?

4. Who was his manager when he first moved to Old Trafford?

5. Which manager first selected him for the England team?

6. How old was he when he made his international debut?

7. Against which country did he score two goals in the 1982 World Cup finals in Spain?

8. Against which club did he score two goals in the 1983 FA Cup Final?

9. He netted a hat-trick against which country in an away match in 1984?

10. Against which club did he lead Manchester United to an FA Cup Final victory in 1985?

ANSWERS

SPORTSWORD (Page 11): ACROSS: 1. Cohen; 7. Boat Race; 8. Lunge; 10. Equestrian; 12. Catcalls; 14. Ends; 16 A Bet; 17. Relay Leg; 20. Kicked Goal; 23. Nurse; 24. Eden Park; 25. Heads. DOWN: 1. Celtic; 2. Edge; 3. Home; 4. State; 5. Nationals; 6. Tennis; 9. Equal; 11. Stretches; 13. Lee; 15. Fagan; 16. Ankles; 18. Greens; 19. Jeeps; 21. Gary; 22. Luge.

Your Score

Running Total

6 SPORTING CINEMA

Each question relates to sports-based films. Two points for each correct answer.
Average score: 8
Greavsie: 10

1. Which athlete was the winner of the Olympic 100 metres final in *Chariots of Fire?*
a) Eric Liddell; b) Harold Abrahams; c) Lord Burghley

2. Ben Hogan was portrayed by which actor in the golfing biopic *Follow the Sun?*
a) Glenn Ford; b) Bing Crosby; c) Gig Young

3. Robert DeNiro featured as which world champion boxer in *Raging Bull?*
a) Rocky Graziano; b) Carmen Basilio; c) Jake LaMotta

4. Which sport provided the background for *Semi Tough,* starring Burt Reynolds and Kris Kristofferson?
a) Baseball; b) Ice Hockey; c) American Football

5. In which race does Paul Newman compete during the climax to the motor racing film, *Winning?*
a) Monaco Grand Prix; b) Indianapolis 500; c) Monte Carlo Rally

6. Who starred as world heavyweight champion James J. Corbett in *Gentleman Jim?*
a) Errol Flynn; b) Clark Gable; c) Ward Bond

7. What is Sylvester Stallone's surname in the series of *Rocky* films?
a) Graziano; b) Mancini; c) Balboa

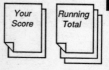

Your Score

Running Total

ANSWERS

THE TRIVIA TEST (Page 12): 1. Cassius Clay (before he became Muhammad Ali); 2. Harry Bradshaw (he was beaten in a play-off for the title by Bobby Locke); 3. Terry Griffiths, 4. Freddie Brown; 5. John Douglas; 6. John Snow; 7. Sonja Henie.

14

7
TEAM
SHEET

There are six famous football teams below, each with a key player missing. Award yourself two points for each absentee that you spot.
Average score: 6
Greavsie: 10

1. ENGLAND'S 1966 WORLD CUP WINNERS
Gordon Banks
George Cohen
Ray Wilson
Nobby Stiles
Bobby Moore
Alan Ball
Roger Hunt
Bobby Charlton
Geoff Hurst
Martin Peters

2. CELTIC'S 1967 EUROPEAN CUP WINNERS
Ronnie Simpson
Jim Craig
Tommy Gemmell
Bobby Murdoch
Billy McNeill
John Clark
Bertie Auld
Willie Wallace
Stevie Chalmers
Bobby Lennox

3. FOREST'S 1979 EUROPEAN CUP WINNERS
Peter Shilton
Viv Anderson
Kenny Burns
Frank Clark
Trevor Francis
John McGovern
Ian Bowyer
John Robertson
Tony Woodcock
Garry Birtles

4. ARSENAL'S 1971 DOUBLE WINNERS
(FA Cup winning team)
Bob Wilson
Pat Rice
Bob McNab
Peter Storey
Frank McLintock
Peter Simpson
George Graham
John Radford
Ray Kennedy
Charlie George
Eddie Kelly (sub)

5. MAN UNITED'S 1985 FA CUP WINNERS
(FA Cup winning team)
Gary Bailey
John Gidman
Arthur Albiston
Norman Whiteside
Paul McGrath
Kevin Moran
Bryan Robson
Gordon Strachan
Mark Hughes
Jesper Olsen
Mike Duxbury (sub)

6. LIVERPOOL'S 1986 DOUBLE WINNERS
(FA Cup winning team)
Bruce Grobbelaar
Mark Lawrenson
Jim Beglin
Steve Nicol
Ronnie Whelan
Jan Molby
Kenny Dalglish
Craig Johnston
Ian Rush
Kevin MacDonald
Steve McMahon (s)

ANSWERS

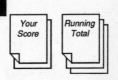

Your Score

Running Total

15

8 GUESS THE GUEST

*See how quickly you can identify
a star sportsman from the clues.*
Average score: 6 Greavsie: 8

For 12 points: Our mystery guest was born in Leicestershire in 1960, and he helped out on his family's market stall before starting his professional sporting career.

For 10 points: His second name is Winston because he shares the same birthday as Winston Churchill.

For 8 points: In 1975 he signed associate schoolboy forms with Leicester City.

For 6 points: He made his debut for England against Scotland at Hampden in 1984, coming on as a substitute for Tony Woodcock.

For 4 points: In June 1985 he was signed by Howard Kendall for £800,000, and in his first season at Goodison Park he was the First Division's top marksman.

For 2 points: He scored against Liverpool in the 1986 FA Cup Final, but he had to be content with a runners-up medal. Terry Venables signed him for Barcelona and he started a new career in the Spanish league after the 1986 World Cup finals.

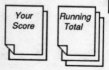

Your Score   Running Total

ANSWERS

⑨ SPORTSTANGLE

Untangle the letters in each of the sections to identify famous sports personalities. Award yourself four points for each correct identification.

Average score: 8 Greavsie: 12

1. Clue: Does he have the widest bat in cricket?

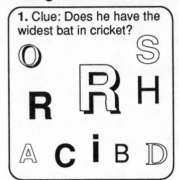

2. Clue: He likes the green green grass of greens!

3. Clue: She has had her golden moments.

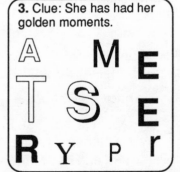

4. Clue: He has really hit the big time.

ANSWERS

TEAM SHEET (Page 15): 1. Jack Charlton; 2. Jimmy Johnstone; 3. Larry Lloyd;
4. George Armstrong; 5. Frank Stapleton; 6. Alan Hansen.

Your Score

Running Total

17

10 SPORTS BOOKSHELF

1. Which motor racing driver had an autobiography published called *Faster!*

a) Jackie Stewart; b) Jim Clark; c) James Hunt

2. Who wrote a novel about boxing called *Cashel Byron's Profession* ?

a) Oscar Wilde; b) George Bernard Shaw; c) W.B.Yeats

3. Which sport features in *The Natural* by Bernard Malamud?

a) Pool; b) Baseball; c) Ice Hockey

4. *The Man They Couldn't Gag* was the best-selling book by which famous sportswriter?

a) Desmond Hackett; b) Tom Phillips; c) Peter Wilson

5. Which all-rounder had a nostalgia book published in 1986 called *Wickets, Catches and the Odd Run?*

a) Ted Dexter; b) Trevor Bailey; c) Ray Illingworth

6. What was the title of Virginia Wade's autobiography?

a) *Courting Triumph*; b) *Jubilee Jubilation*; c) *A Winning Racquet*

7. About which manager was a book written called *Father of Football?*

a) Joe Mercer; b) Bill Shankly; c) Matt Busby

8. Who wrote *The Fight,* a book based on the 'Rumble in the Jungle' between Muhammad Ali and George Foreman?

a) Bud Schulberg; b) Irwin Shaw; c) Norman Mailer

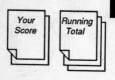

Your Score | Running Total

ANSWERS

GUESS THE GUEST (Page 16): The mystery personality is England international footballer Gary Lineker, the Barcelona and former Leicester City and Everton striker.

11 THE NAME GAME

EACH clue leads to a well-known name. Put the initials in the appropriate squares to identify a sports star: Two points for each correct answer, plus a bonus of ten points for completing the main name.

Average score: 20 Greavsie: 22

1	2	3	4	5	6	7

8	9	10	11	12	13

3 & 9	'The Eagle' who landed last in Calgary but first in the publicity stakes.
4 & 6	His wife booked herself for fame while he was bowling for England.
12 & 5	This Anfield marksman helped to shoot England to victory in the 1966 World Cup.
7	Surname of the lady who has dominated Wimbledon since leaving Prague.
2 & 13	The ex-Coventry, Leeds and Spurs star who has been a soccer prince of Wales.
1 & 11	He is always at the head of the table, and is known as the 'Ginger Magician.'
10 & 8	This former England defender was famed and feared for the bite in his tackle.

ANSWERS

SPORTSTANGLE (Page 17): 1. Chris Broad; 2. Ian Woosnam; 3. Mary Peters; 4. Mike Tyson.

Your Score

Running Total

12 ON A PLATE

Here are 15 easy questions to help you boost your score. Award yourself a point for each correct answer, plus a one point bonus every time that you get three successive questions right.
Average score: 13 Greavsie: 18

1. Which Football League team is at home at Maine Road?

2. From which Jamaican did Mike Tyson take the world title?

3. With which club did Peter Beardsley start his career?

4. Which batsman has scored most runs in Test match cricket?

5. How many times did Red Rum win the Grand National?

6. Who won the 1987 men's Wimbledon singles title?

7. In which event was Bob Beamon an Olympic champion?

8. Who won the 1987 flat racing jockeys' championship?

9. With which sport do you associate the name Nelli Kim?

10. On which ground do Middlesex usually play home games?

11. Duncan Goodhew specialised in which swimming stroke?

12. What nationality is skier Franz Klammer?

13. Who had his first Derby winner on Never Say Die?

14. With which club did Tom Finney spend his entire career?

15. Brian Statham was a bowler with which County?

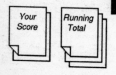

Your Score | Running Total

ANSWERS

13 SPORTS SQUARE

The answers in this Sports Square overlap. Award yourself one point for each correct answer and a five-point bonus if you complete the square.
Average score: 12
Greavsie: 18

1a: Digs hall to find a football manager (8)
1d: Bradman, or perhaps Howe (3)
4d: Charlie, who challenged Jim Watt (4)
5d: A duelling sword for fencers (4)
7d: Wes, who bowled at lightning speed (4)

2a: He emerged from the shadow of Banks (7)
2d: Gatting likes to do it in reverse (5)
3d: Webb, Adcock or perhaps Harvey (4)
6d: This Austrian is an ace at the wheel (5)
9a: Winners of the 1966 World Cup (7)

8a: Bare need for a team at Pittodrie (8)
8d: He is hunting vintage goals in Bordeaux (5)
12d: He was runner-up at Wimbledon in 1984 (5)
15a: They play basketball in Los Angeles (6)
16a: You should find them doing it at Bisley (8)

9d: You will find Reading at this Park (3)
10d: Are you desperate to be one at judo? (3)
11d: Fisherman do this to a degree (5)
13d: Rodney, of football or cricket fame (5).
14d: One often becomes before a wicket (3)

ANSWERS

THE NAME GAME (Page 19): Scottish snooker star STEPHEN HENDRY (Eddie Edwards, Phil Edmonds, Roger Hunt, (Martina) Navratilova, Terry Yorath, Steve Davis, Norman Hunter).

Your Score

Running Total

14 BEHIND THE WHEEL

Award yourself two points for each correct answer to these motor racing questions **Average score: 6 Greavsie: 8**

1. Which car was Niki Lauda driving when he won the world championship in 1977?

a) JPS Lotus-Ford; b) Ferrari; c) McLaren

2. Who won the 1987 world drivers' championship with 79 points?

a) Nelson Piquet; b) Ayrton Senna; c) Alain Prost

3. What nationality is South American driving master Emerson Fittipaldi?

a) Brazilian; b) Bolivian; c) Argentinian

4. Which British driver raced in 90 consecutive Grand Prixs in the 1960s?

a) Stirling Moss; b) Jackie Stewart; c) Graham Hill

5. How old was Juan-Manuel Fangio when he last won the world title?

a) 38; b) 42; c) 46

6. Which American driver won the Indianapolis 500 for a fourth time in 1987?

a) Al Unser; b) Rick Mears; c) Bobby Rahal

7. On which motor racing track is Woodcote Corner?

a) Brands Hatch; b) Silverstone; c) Brooklands

8. Who won the 1966 world title in a car that he built himself?

a) Bruce McLaren; b) Jack Brabham; c) John Surtees

Your Score

Running Total

ANSWERS

ON A PLATE (Page 20): 1. Manchester City; 2. Trevor Berbick; 3. Carlisle; 4. Sunil Gavaskar; 5. Three times; 6. Pat Cash; 7. Long Jump; 8. Steve Cauthen; 9. Gymnastics; 10. Lord's; 11. Breast stroke; 12. Austrian; 13. Lester Piggott; 14. Preston; 15. Lancashire

22

15
ALL ★ AMERICAN

There are 7 questions here about the American sports scene. Two points for each correct answer.
Average score: 6 Greavsie: 8

1. Joe Namath was an outstanding quarterback player with which American football team?

    a) New York Jets; b) Chicago Bears; c) New York Giants

2. What, including the end zones, is the standard length of an American football field?

    a) 100 yards; b) 120 yards; c) 140 yards

3. Ralph Greenleaf was world champion across two decades in which favourite American sport?

    a) Tenpin bowling; b) Handball; c) Pool

4. Which is the first leg of the American Triple Crown in horse racing?

    a) Belmont Stakes; b) Preakness Stakes; c) Kentucky Derby

5. The Tennessee Tigerbelles became famous in which field of sport?

    a) Hockey; b) Sprint relay running; c) Volleyball

6. What were the real first names of legendary baseball hero Babe Ruth?

    a) Elmer Theodore; b) Mervyn Washington; c) George Herman

7. Which sport would you be watching if you were supporting the New York Knickerbockers?

    a) Ice hockey; b) Baseball; c) Basketball

ANSWERS

Your Score

Running Total

16
WHAT'S HIS NAME...?

There are 20 sportsmen on this page labelled only by their nick-name. Award yourself one point for each correct identification.
Average score: 12
Greavsie: 13

1. Brown Bomber (Boxing)

2. The Gentle Giant (Football)

3. Barnacle (Cricket)

4. Superbrat (Tennis) **5.** The Grinder (Snooker)

6. Smokin' Joe (Boxing) **7.** Little Bird (Cricket)

8. Golden Vision (Football) **9.** Leamington Licker (Boxing)

10. The Tinman (Horse Racing) **11.** Stroller (Football)

12. Real Deal (Boxing) **13.** Fat Boy (Football)

14. Clones Cyclone (Boxing) **15.** Der Bomber (Football)

16. Toothless Tiger (Football) **17.** The Gnome (Cricket)

18. The Old Dancing Master (Rugby Union)

19. Galveston Giant (Boxing) **20.** Chippy (Football)

Your Score

Running Total

ANSWERS

BEHIND THE WHEEL (Page 22): 1. Ferrari; 2. Nelson Piquet; 3. Brazilian; 4. Graham Hill; 5. 46 years old; 6. Al Unser; 7. Silverstone; 8. Jack Brabham.

17 SPORTS SLEUTH

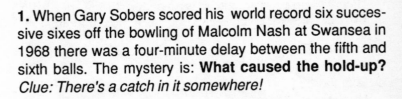

Here are four sporting mysteries for you to solve. Award yourself four points for each correct answer.
Average score: 4 Greavsie: 8

1. When Gary Sobers scored his world record six successive sixes off the bowling of Malcolm Nash at Swansea in 1968 there was a four-minute delay between the fifth and sixth balls. The mystery is: **What caused the hold-up?** *Clue: There's a catch in it somewhere!*

2. Rocky Marciano, the only world heavyweight champion to retire undefeated, had one of his earliest fights in South Wales. The mystery is: **Why is the fight not in the record books?** *Clue: It was a public fight of sorts.*

3. Italian skipper Peppino Meazza scored from the penalty spot against Brazil to clinch a place in the 1938 World Cup Final. The mystery is: **Why did he later describe it as one of the most embarrassing moments of his life?** *Clue: Could it have been described as a drop goal?*

4. Lester Piggott finished second in the 1952 Derby on Gay Time, and as he went past the post he decided to object to the winner Tulyar. The mystery is: **Why didn't the stewards hear Lester's objection?** *Clue: Was Lester feeling a little off at the time?*

ANSWERS

ALL AMERICAN (Page 23): 1. New York Jets; 2. 120 yards; 3. Pool; 4. Kentucky Derby; 5. Sprint Relay Running; 6. George Herman; 7. Basketball.

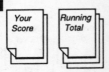

18
HARK WHO'S TALKING

There are quotes on this page from six famous sports personalities. Score two points for each that you correctly identify.
Average score: 4 Greavsie: 6

1. "People who say that football is a matter of life and death don't know what they're talking about. It's much more important than that."
a) Brian Clough; b) Bill Shankly; c) Malcolm Allison

2. "For those of you watching in black and white, Tottenham are wearing the yellow shirts."
a) Barry Davies; b) David Coleman; c) John Motson

3. "I know that I'm different from Australian players of the past. Can you imagine any of them wearing a diamond in their ear?"
a) Jeff Thomson; b) Greg Norman; c) Pat Cash

4. "The bell went ding and I went dong!"
a) Frank Bruno; b) Lloyd Honeyghan; c) Nigel Benn

5. "You wouldn't treat a dog the way I've been treated. In some ways I'm glad to be going because you don't want to work for people like that."
a) John Bond; b) Lawrie McMenemy; c) Tommy Docherty

6. "In tennis the public would rather watch John McEnroe or Jimmy Connors than Ivan Lendl or Bjorn Borg. It's the same in snooker. The public will flock to watch me or Stephen Hendry before they cough up to watch Steve Davis. People want to be entertained."
a) Jimmy White; b) Tony Knowles; c) Alex Higgins

ANSWERS

WHAT'S HIS NAME? (Page 24): 1. Joe Louis 2. John Charles; 3. Trevor Bailey; 4. John McEnroe; 5. Cliff Thorburn; 6. Joe Frazier; 7. Curtley Ambrose; 8. Alex Young; 9. Randolph Turpin; 10. Fred Archer; 11. George Graham; 12. Evander Holyfield; 13. Paul Gascoigne; 14. Barry McGuigan; 15. Gerd Mueller; 16. Nobby Stiles; 17. Keith Fletcher; 18. Peter Jackson; 19. Jack Johnson; 20. Liam Brady.

Do you know your way around the sports world? This will test you. One point each time you know where you are. **Average score: 5 Greavsie: 7**

Where are you when you're watching...

1. League football at Plainmoor

2. Test cricket at Headingley

3. The Oaks

4. The US Masters golf championship

5. World title boxing at Madison Square Garden

6. The British hardcourt tennis championships

7. Athletics in the stadium built for the 1964 Olympics

8. The Irish Sweepstakes Derby

9. Italian League football at the San Siro stadium

10. Test cricket in the land of Colin Cowdrey's birth

ANSWERS

SPORTS SLEUTH ANSWER: 1. The umpires were debating whether Sobers had been caught off the fifth ball, but they finally ruled that the fielder fell over the boundary when taking the catch; 2. Rocky was based in South Wales with the US Army during the Second World War. An Australian soldier insulted him in a public house and legend has it that Rocky laid him out with a swinging right to the jaw; 3. As he took the penalty, Peppino's shorts—torn earlier in the game—slipped down to leave him more exposed than the Brazilian goalkeeper; 4. Lester was thrown by Gay Time after passing the post. By the time he had caught his horse and weighed-in the stewards ruled that he was too late to lodge an objection.

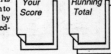

20 TEE TIME

You score two points for each correct answer in this round of golfing questions
Average score: 6 Greavsie: 8

1. On which course did Tom Watson set a British Open record of 268 when beating Jack Nicklaus by one shot in 1977?
a) Turnberry; b) Royal Birkdale; c) St Andrews

2. Who scored a final round of 63 to clinch victory in the US Open in 1973?
a) Jack Nicklaus; b) Gary Player; c) Johnny Miller

3. Who did Ian Woosnam beat by one up to win the 1987 world matchplay championship?
a) Sandy Lyle; b) Sam Torrance; c) Nick Faldo

4. Lanny Wadkins was pipped in a play-off for the US PGA title in 1987 by which player?
a) Tom Kite; b) Hale Irwin; c) Larry Nelson

5. Who was runner-up to 1988 US Masters champion Sandy Lyle?
a) Greg Norman; b) Mark Calcavecchia; c) Craig Stadler

6. On which course did Tony Jacklin win the British Open in 1969?
a) Royal Lytham & St Annes; b) Carnoustie; c) Royal Birkdale

7. Which non-American won the US Masters and the Heritage Classic in successive weeks on the US circuit in 1985?
a) Seve Ballesteros; b) Bernhard Langer; c) David Graham

Your Score

Running Total

ANSWERS

HARK WHO'S TALKING (Page 26): 1.Bill Shankly; 2. John Motson; 3. Pat Cash; 4. Lloyd Honeyghan (after knocking down Johnny Bumphus with the first punch of round two of their world title fight); 5. John Bond (after his dismissal by Birmingham City); 6. Alex Higgins.

21 HOW WELL D'YOU KNOW...?

MIKE TYSON

Award yourself one point for each question you can answer about boxer Mike Tyson

Average score: 5 Greavsie: 7

1. In which borough of New York City was he born?

2. Who was the famous old boxing manager who discovered him while he was in a remand home?

3. Which former world handball champion became his joint manager?

4. In which year did he make his professional debut?

5. What is his ring nickname?

6. Who is the ex-professional boxer who has trained him for all of his contests?

7. After how many fights did Tyson become the youngest ever world heavyweight champion—24, 26 or 28?

8. How old was he when he first won the title?

9. Who was the first opponent to go the full distance with him in a non-title fight?

10. Who did he beat to become the undisputed triple world title holder in 1987?

ANSWERS

GOING PLACES (Page 27): 1. Torquay; 2. Leeds; 3. Epsom; 4. Augusta, Georgia; 5. New York City; 6. Bournemouth; 7. Tokyo; 8. The Curragh; 9. Milan; 10. India.

Your Score

Running Total

There are three sets of six questions on tennis here. Award yourself one point for each correct answer and a bonus of five points if you get at least four right in each set. **Average score: 9 Greavsie: 12**

FIRST SET

1. Who was the first left handed women's Wimbledon champion?
a) Margaret Scriven; b) Ann Jones; c) Kay Stammers
2. What nationality is Tom Okker?
a) Austrian; b) Danish; c) Dutch
3. In which year did Virginia Wade become Wimbledon champion?
a) 1976; b) 1977; c) 1978
4. With whom did John Newcombe have most doubles successes?
a) Tony Roche; b) Owen Davidson; c) Ken Rosewall
5. Which Wimbledon champion was the son of a High Court judge?
a) Frank Sedgman; b) Dick Savitt; c) Neale Fraser
6. Who was runner-up to John McEnroe at Wimbledon in 1983?
a) Kevin Curren; b) Chris Lewis; c) Roscoe Tanner

SECOND SET

1. Who was an officer in the US Army when ranked world No 1?
a) Stan Smith; b) Tony Trabert; c) Vic Seixas
2. What nationality was Maria Bueno?
a) Peruvian; b) Brazilian; c) Mexican
3. In which year did Bjorn Borg win his last Wimbledon title?
a) 1979; b) 1980; c) 1981
4. Who was the second woman to complete the Grand Slam?
a) Maureen Connolly; b) Evonne Goolagong; c) Margaret Court
5. Which of these players was never a Wimbledon singles champion?
a) Jack Kramer; b) Budge Patty; c) Pancho Gonzales
6. Who was Rod Laver's opponent in 3 finals in his 1962 Grand Slam year?
a) Martin Mulligan; b) Roy Emerson; c) Fred Stolle

THIRD SET

1. Who won the US Open at 16?
a) Pam Shriver; b) Tracy Austin; c) Hana Mandlikova
2. Who was Australian champion at the age of 37 in 1972?
a) Lew Hoad; b) Ken Fletcher; c) Ken Rosewall
3. To which country did Jaroslav Drobny first defect?
a) Egypt; b) France; c) Holland
4. How many times was Fred Perry Wimbledon champion?
a) Three; b) Four; c) Five
5. Which country knocked the USA out of the 1987 Davis Cup?
a) Argentina; b) Mexico; c) Paraguay
6. Who completed a hat-trick of US title wins in 1987?
a) Ivan Lendl; b) Boris Becker; c) Jimmy Connors

 Your Score / *Running Total*

 ANSWERS

TEE TIME (Page 28): 1. Turnberry; 2. Johnny Miller; 3. Sandy Lyle; 4. Larry Nelson; 5. Mark Calcavecchia; 6. Royal Lytham & St Annes; 7. Bernhard Langer.

23 SEARCH FOR A STAR

How many British Olympic gold medallists can you find in this grid? There are 15 names. Some appear in straightforward, left-to-right formations, others are printed in reverse or diagonally across the page. Award yourself one point for each name that you find.
Average score: 9 Greavsie: 11

```
L D A E R B T I H W C
O V E T T M K P N E O
N D Y R E M E H S L E
S P A H L G R A Q L S
B E N V X B E R D S M
R T G E I K L I W E A
O E L A N E T Y M D H
U R H S X F S P J N A
G S W E H D O O G A R
H F I N N E G A N R B
R X N O S P M O H T A
```

Your Score

Running Total

31

*Award yourself two points for
each correct answer to these
American Football questions.*
Average score: 4 Greavsie: 6

1. Who amassed a record 18 points for San Francisco 49ers in the 1985 Super Bowl?
a) Ray Wersching; b) Joe Montana; c) Roger Craig

2. With which team has Dan Marino made his reputation as one of the greats of Gridiron?
a) Miami Dolphins; b) Dallas Cowboys; c) Los Angeles Raiders

3. In a game of American football each team has 'four downs' to try to travel what distance?
a) 10 yards; b) 20 yards; c) 15 yards

4. Who in 1984 set a Super Bowl rushing record of 191 yards?
a) Walter Payton; b) Eric Dickerson; c) Marcus Allen

5. Of which team was the legendary Vince Lombardi one of the most successful coaches in the history of the sport?
a) Pittsburgh Steelers; b) New York Jets; c) Green Bay Packers

6. In which city are the Seahawks based?
a) Chicago; b) Minneapolis; c) Seattle

7. Which Olympic 100 metres gold medallist became a top-flight American footballer?
a) Bob Hayes; b) Bobby-Joe Morrow; c) Lindy Remigino

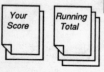

Your Score   Running Total

ANSWERS

ANYONE FOR TENNIS? (Page 30): **Set 1**— 1. Ann Jones; 2. Dutch; 3. 1977; 4. Tony Roche; 5. Neale Fraser; 6. Chris Lewis.   **Set 2**—1. Stan Smith; 2. Brazilian; 3. 1980; 4. Margaret Court; 5. Pancho Gonzales; 6. Roy Emerson. **Set 3**—1. Tracy Austin; 2. Ken Rosewall; 3. France; 4. Three times; 5. Paraguay; 6. Ivan Lendl.

25
SPORTS GRAM

Rearrange the letters to identify a team of 11 international footballers. We give a brief clue to help you. Award yourself two points for each correct answer.
Average score: 10 Greavsie: 16

1. **OVAL NUTSHELL LIE**
He handles with care for Wales

2. **DROVE IN VANS**
He went from Highbury to Old Trafford

3. **NAN'S MONKEYS**
He lifted the League Cup in 1987

4. **GO-CART AND HORNS**
He started out with Aberdeen

5. **CRY BEER TRUTH**
He is at home on both sides of the border

6. **DEEP TRIER**
He no doubt takes a coach to Goodison

7. **TRY A BED SLEEPER**
He is a Geordie with Scouse connections

8. **FRAME NECK IN VAN**
He was a Hammer before returning hame

9. **LINED HARD JOG**
He once passed with honours at Oxford

10. **HUG HER MASK**
He has scored in Spain and Germany

11. **CHILD SAW RED**
He winged his way from Tyneside to Tottenham

ANSWERS

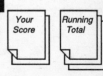

Your Score

Running Total

Award yourself two points for each marathon master that you identify. The answers, but not in order, are Kevin Forster, Belaine Dinsamo, Emil Zatopek, Derek Clayton, Carlos Lopes, Jim Peters, Ian Thompson, Alberto Salazar.

Average score: 8 Greavsie: 10

1. The English-born Australian who set a world's best marathon time that lasted 12 years until 1981.

2. The Geordie who chased Dane Henrik Jorgensen home in second place in the 1988 London marathon.

3. The Cuban-born runner who won the 1980 New York City championship in his first marathon run.

4. The man who clocked a world's best 2hr 6m 49s in Rotterdam in 1988.

5. The 1948 Olympic 10,000 metres gold medallist who won the 1952 Olympic marathon in his first attempt at the distance.

6. The Essex optician who set world best times for the marathon four times between 1952 and 1954.

7. The Luton schoolteacher who won the European championship in 1974

8. The Portuguese who won the gold medal in the 1984 Olympics in Los Angeles.

ANSWERS

Your Score | Running Total

GRIDIRON GRILLING (Page 32): 1. Roger Craig; 2. Miami Dolphins; 3. 10 yards; 4. Marcus Allen; 5. Green Bay Packers; 6. Seattle; 7. Bob Hayes.

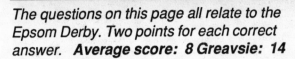

The questions on this page all relate to the Epsom Derby. Two points for each correct answer. **Average score: 8 Greavsie: 14**

1. On which horse did Willie Carson ride his first Derby winner at Epsom in 1979?
   a) Shirley Heights; b) Troy; c) Henbit

2. Which jockey had his only Derby victory on Snow Knight in 1974?
   a) Eddie Hide; b) Frankie Durr; c) Brian Taylor

3. Which trainer saddled 1982 Derby winner Golden Fleece?
   a) Peter Walwyn; b) Vincent O'Brien; c) Dick Hern

4. Shergar was a winner for which owner?
   a) Robert Sangster; b) Sir Michael Sobell; c) Aga Khan

5. Who was the first jockey to ride two post-war Derby winners?
   a) Lester Piggott; b) Charlie Smirke; c) Rae Johnstone

6. On which horse did Lester Piggott have his only odds-on winner in the Derby?
   a) Nijinsky; b) Sir Ivor; c) Roberto

7. Which horse holds the record for the fastest Derby?
   a) Shahrastani; b) Mahmoud; c) Sea Bird II

8. Which horse finished second to Kahyasi in the 1988 Derby?
   a) Glacial Storm; b) Minster Son; c) Doyoun

ANSWERS

SPORTS GRAM (Page 33): 1. Neville Southall; 2. Viv Anderson; 3. Kenny Sansom; 4. Gordon Strachan; 5. Terry Butcher; 6. Peter Reid; 7. Peter Beardsley; 8. Frank McAvennie; 9. John Aldridge; 10. Mark Hughes; 11. Chris Waddle.

Your Score

Running Total

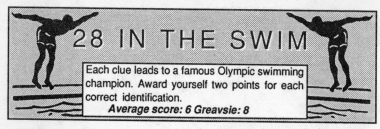

28 IN THE SWIM

Each clue leads to a famous Olympic swimming champion. Award yourself two points for each correct identification.
Average score: 6 Greavsie: 8

1. This **Australian** won a record eight medals in the Olympics of 1956, 1960 and 1964, including four golds. She captured the 100 metres freestyle title in three successive Olympics, and during her career set 39 world records.

2. This **American** won 52 US titles, broke 28 world records and was the first man to duck under the one-minute barrier in the 100 metres freestyle. He collected five Olympic gold medals, and then became world famous as the best known of the Hollywood Tarzans.

3. This **East German** set or equalled four world records on her way to collecting four gold medals in the 1976 Olympics in Montreal. She was an exceptional all-rounder, equally supreme in the freestyle and butterfly events.

4. This **British** champion—a 19-year-old Huddersfield girl—won the 200 metres breast-stroke gold medal in the 1960 Olympics in Rome. On her way to victory she became the first woman to break the 2min 50sec barrier.

5. This **American** dental student rewrote the Olympic record books at Munich in 1972 with seven gold medals, breaking world records in each event in which he competed. He also won two golds in the 1968 Games.

6. This American-trained **Scot** won the gold medal in the 200 metres breast-stroke in Montreal in the 1976 Games, and took the silver medal in the 100 metres event. He made an international comeback in 1988.

Your Score

Running Total

ANSWERS

THE CRICKET TEST 1

There are 100 points to be scored in this 5-page test of your cricket knowledge. Fill in the blanks and award yourself two points for each correct answer. *Average score: 48 Greavsie: 54*

1 [　　　　　　] scored 17 centuries in the summer of 1947 while playing for England and Middlesex.

2 [　　　　　　] took 19 wickets for England against Australia in the 1956 Test at Old Trafford.

3 [　　　　　　] held 1,473 catches behind the wicket for Derbyshire and England between 1960 and 1986.

4 [　　　　　　] took ten Nottinghamshire wickets for ten runs with his left arm spin bowling for Yorkshire in 1932.

5 [　　　　　　] scored 364 for England against Australia in the 1938 Test at The Oval.

6 [　　　　　　] played in a record 114 Tests for England between 1950 and 1976.

7 [　　　　　　] became England's youngest Test cricketer at 18 against New Zealand at Old Trafford in 1949?

8 [　　　　　　] was 45 when he made his final appearance for England against the West Indies at Old Trafford in 1976.

9 [　　　　　　] skippered the England team beaten by Australia in the Centenary Test at Melbourne in 1977.

10 [　　　　　　] played a record 65 consecutive Tests for England between 1977 and 1984?

ANSWERS

FIRST PAST THE POST (Page 35): 1. Troy; 2. Brian Taylor; 3. Vincent O'Brien; 4. Aga Khan; 5. Rae Johnstone; 6. Sir Ivor; 7. Mahmoud; 8. Glacial Storm

Your Score *Running Total*

THE CRICKET TEST 2

11 [ ] completed the double of 1,000 runs and 100 wickets with Notts in 1984.

12 [ ] scored an English record 8,114 runs in Test cricket while playing 108 matches.

13 [ ] shared an English record opening stand of 555 with Percy Holmes for Yorkshire against Essex in 1932.

14 [ ] scored 306 not out in an Australian record stand of 462 for South Australia against Tasmania in 1987.

15 [ ] was England wicket-keeper in 95 Tests and amassed 4,389 runs.

16 [ ] took over as Australia's top Test runmaker with an innings of 205 against India in 1987.

17 [ ] set a world Test record of 365 against Pakistan in Kingston in 1957-58.

18 [ ] took 14 England wickets for 149 runs for the West Indies at The Oval in 1976.

19 [ ] played for Sussex, captained Pakistan and took more than 260 Test wickets.

20 [ ] scored 309 runs in one day for Australia against England at Headingley in 1930.

ANSWERS

Your Score   Running Total

IN THE SWIM (Page 36): 1. Dawn Fraser; 2. Johnny Weissmuller; 3. Kornelia Ender; 4. Anita Lonsbrough; 5. Mark Spitz; 6. David Wilkie.

THE CRICKET TEST 3

21 [＿＿＿＿＿] topped the batting averages in 1987 with 1,627 runs for Somerset.

22 [＿＿＿＿＿] bowled a record 129 overs in a Test match for the West Indies against England at Edgbaston in 1957.

23 [＿＿＿＿＿] held a Test record 122 catches in 87 Tests for Australia between 1970-71 and 1983-84?

24 [＿＿＿＿＿] blitzed the Australians with 6 for 16 off 51 deliveries in the third Test of England's 1954-55 tour.

25 [＿＿＿＿＿] was the only bowler to take all 10 wickets three times in first-class cricket while playing for Kent.

26 [＿＿＿＿＿] opened the batting for New Zealand and Worcestershire and scored 34,346 first class runs.

27 [＿＿＿＿＿] amassed an all-time record 197 centuries while playing for Surrey and England.

28 [＿＿＿＿＿] hit the boundary 50 times in a hurricane innings of 322 for Somerset against Warwickshire.

29 [＿＿＿＿＿] scored 102 centuries for Warwickshire and England before retiring in 1987.

30 [＿＿＿＿＿] was the first bowler to take more than 300 Test wickets.

ANSWERS

THE CRICKET TEST 1 (Page 37): 1. Denis Compton; 2. Jim Laker; 3. Bob Taylor; 4. Hedley Verity; 5. Len Hutton; 6. Colin Cowdrey; 7. Brian Close; 8. Brian Close; 9. Tony Greig; 10. Ian Botham.

Your Score	Running Total

THE CRICKET TEST 4

31 [_____] succeeded Pat Pocock as captain of Surrey for the start of the 1987 County cricket season.

32 [_____] succeeded David Gower as captain of England and scored his first Test century in his 31st match.

33 [_____] played for Gloucestershire, was known as 'The Champion' and was a doctor by profession.

34 [_____] was one of the greatest of all Aussie left-handed batsmen who bagged a pair at Old Trafford in 1956.

35 [_____] scored a hundred for India in each of his first three Test matches in 1984-85.

36 [_____] took 33 wickets for England in the 'Bodyline' tour and later emigrated to Australia.

37 [_____] was the first batsman to pass a total of 10,000 runs in Test match cricket.

38 [_____] captained Australia against Mike Brearley's England and later scored 1,834 runs for Victoria in 1983.

39 [_____] was nicknamed 'Deadly' and became the youngest bowler to take 100 wickets in a season in 1963.

40 [_____] was the leading wicket-taker in Test cricket until overtaken by Ian Botham.

Your Score

Running Total

ANSWERS

THE CRICKET TEST 5

41 [_____]was a spinner with Yorkshire and Leicester-shire and captained England in Australia in 1971.

42 [_____]took 236 wickets for England and twice dismissed Don Bradman for a duck in Test cricket.

43 [_____]played for Surrey as a medium-pace bowler and took a Test hat-trick against the West Indies in 1957.

44 [_____]captained England and later became the Bishop of Liverpool

45 [_____]became the second player to hit six success-ive sixes off an over in 1985 and plays for India.

46 [_____]scored a double century for England against India at Madras in 1985, along with Mike Gatting.

47 [_____]was the first player to hold 100 Test catches and captained England in the immediate post-war years.

48 [_____]took 16 wickets for 137 runs in his Test debut for Australia against England at Lord's in 1972.

49 [_____]scored 337 Test runs for Pakistan against West Indies in a marathon 16-hour innings.

50 [_____]took a victory-clinching 8 for 43 for Eng-land against Australia at Headingley in 1981.

ANSWERS

THE CRICKET TEST 3 (Page 39): 21. Martin Crowe; 22. Sonny Ramadhin;
23. Greg Chappell; 24. Frank Tyson; 25. Alfred (Tich) Freeman; 26. Glenn
Turner; 27. Jack Hobbs; 28. Viv Richards; 29. Dennis Amiss; 30. Fred Trueman.

Can you fill in the blanks in the following sporting headlines? Award yourself one point for each gap that you fill.
Average score: 7
Greavsie: 10

1.
BLANK STOPS ALAN MINTER IN 3RD TO WIN WORLD TITLE

2.
POWELL RIDES BLANK TO 1988 NATIONAL TRIUMPH

3.
BLANK'S TWO GOALS CLINCH WEMBLEY VICTORY FOR LUTON

4.
FALDO WINS BRITISH OPEN WITH 18 PARS AT BLANK

5.
BLANK PIPS LEWIS TO WIN 100 METRES WORLD TITLE

6.
BLANK SENT OFF AT WEMBLEY IN ANGRY WORLD CUP CLASH AGAINST ENGLAND

7.
BOTHAM SACKED BY BLANK AFTER BUST-UP ON 'PLANE

8.
BLANK BEAT HULL 28-24 IN CLASSIC 1985 CUP FINAL

9.
BLANK CONQUERS CURREN TO BECOME THE YOUNGEST WIMBLEDON CHAMP

10.
BLANK KOs JOHANSSON TO BECOME THE FIRST MAN TO REGAIN TITLE

11.
TESSA'S GOLDEN THROW WINS HER AN OLYMPIC TITLE AT BLANK

12.
BLANK STOPS BUGNER IN 8

13.
BLANK TAKES SILVER IN MUNICH ON PSALM

14.
BLANK NETS HIS 49TH GOAL FOR SPURS

ANSWERS

Your Score

Running Total

THE CRICKET TEST 4 (Page 40): 31. Ian Greig; 32. Mike Gatting; 33. WG Grace; 34. Neil Harvey; 35. Azharuddin; 36. Harold Larwood; 37. Sunil Gavaskar; 38. Graham Yallop; 39. Derek Underwood; 40. Dennis Lillee.

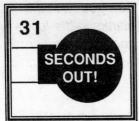

31

SECONDS OUT!

You have got to go 10 rounds with 10 different boxers who have all held British titles since 1980. Award yourself two points each time you can identify your opponent. Give yourself a ten point knockout bonus if you can name 8 or more.
Average score: 8 Greavsie: 10

Round 1: This Welshman succeeded Charlie Magri as British eight-stone champion by knocking out Dave George in six rounds at Wembley in 1982.

Round 2: A brave warrior from Hartlepool, he won the British bantamweight title on the same night that his brother became lightweight champion.

Round 3: Your nine-stone opponent won a Lonsdale Belt outright in 1980 and gave up the title after becoming European champion.

Round 4: Now you're in against a lightweight from Balham who was in the same Terry Lawless stable as world champion Jim Watt.

Round 5: Coming out from the light-welterweight corner is the Croydon fighter whose younger brother later became the flyweight champion.

Round 6: This Jamaican-born, Bermondsey-based welterweight went on to rule the world after relinquishing the British title.

Round 7: Your light-middleweight opponent is a southpaw from Sheffield who later moved up a division to hunt for the world 11st 6lb title.

Round 8: A West Hammer comes out fighting for the middleweights. He has since moved up to light-heavyweight.

Round 9: This larruper from Leeds won the vacant British light-heavyweight title by outpointing Dennis Andries.

Round 10: Finally, you are matched against Frank Bruno's stablemate who is based in Birmingham.

ANSWERS

THE CRICKET TEST (Page 41): 41. Ray Illingworth; 42. Alec Bedser; 43. Peter Loader; 44. David Sheppard; 45. Ravi Shastri; 46. Graeme Fowler; 47. Wally Hammond; 48. Bob Massie; 49. Hanif Mohammad; 50. Bob Willis.

See how quickly you can identify a sports personality from the clues.
Average score: 4 Greavsie: 6

For 12 points: Our mystery guest was born in Yapton, Sussex, in 1957, and first started to make a name for himself in his sport as a schoolboy at Millfield.

For 10 points: He became an international star after coming under the expert coaching influence of Dave Haller.

For 8 points: It was after taking a sports scholarship in the United States that he made the breakthrough to world class, and he was a finalist in the 1976 Olympics in Montreal.

For 6 points: Four years later in the Moscow Olympics he struck gold and also picked up a bronze as a member of the British relay squad.

For 4 points: A member of the Beckenham Swimming Club, he emerged from the shadow of David Wilkie and captained the Great Britain team in the 1980 Games.

For 2 points: Distinctive because of his bald head, he was the 1980 Olympic gold medallist at his speciality event over 100 metres.

Your Score

Running Total

ANSWERS

HEADLINE MAKERS (Page 42): 1. Marvin Hagler; 2. Rhyme 'n' Reason; 3. Brian Stein; 4. Muirfield; 5. Ben Johnson; 6. Antonio Rattin; 7. Queensland; 8. Wigan; 9. Boris Becker; 10. Floyd Patterson; 11. Los Angeles; 12. Frank Bruno; 13. Ann Moore; 14. Clive Allen.

SEBASTIAN COE

*Award yourself one point for each
question you can answer about
athlete Sebastian Coe*
Average score: 4 Greavsie: 6

1. In which city was he based when first starting out on his career?

2. At which university was he studying when he made the breakthrough as an international force?

3. Who has been his coach and advisor ever since his schoolboy days?

4. In which three events did he set world records during a span of 41 days in 1979?

5. In which event did he set a world record of 2m. 12.8s.?

6. Who won the 1980 Olympic 800 metres final in which he had to be satisfied with a silver medal?

7. Did he set an Olympic record when winning the 1980 Olympic 1500 metres gold medal — yes or no?

8. Which of his 1981 world records was still intact seven years later?

9. In which city did he lower the mile record to 3m. 47.33s.?

10. Who was runner-up when he retained the Olympic 1500 metres title in Los Angeles in 1984?

ANSWERS

SECONDS OUT (Page 43): 1. Kelvin Smart; 2. John Feeney; 3. Pat Cowdell; 4. Ray Cattouse; 5. Clinton McKenzie; 6. Lloyd Honeyghan; 7. Herol Graham; 8. Mark Kaylor; 9. Tom Collins; 10. Horace Notice.

Your Score

Running Total

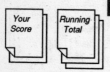

A SCORE OF SCORERS

There are 20 questions in this quiz all relating to goal scorers. Award yourself one point for each question that you answer correctly.

Average score: 9 Greavsie: 15

1. Who was top goal scorer in the 1966 World Cup finals tournament in England?

a) Geoff Hurst; b) Eusebio; c) Helmut Haller

2. Against which team did Stan Mortensen score an FA Cup Final hat-trick at Wembley in 1953?

a) Bolton Wanderers; b) Aston Villa; c) Manchester City

3. Ray Crawford scored 203 League goals for which club?

a) Wolves; b) Portsmouth; c) Ipswich Town

4. Who netted Aston Villa's European Cup Final winner in 1982?

a) Gary Shaw; b) Peter Withe; c) Gordon Cowans

5. How many goals did Bobby Charlton net in 106 England games?

a) 49; b) 59; c) 69

6. Who was top goal scorer in the 1986 World Cup finals in Mexico?

a) Diego Maradona; b) Karl-Heinz Rummenigge; c) Gary Lineker

7. Which striker scored 9 goals in an FA Cup tie for Bournemouth?

a) Phil Boyer; b) Ted MacDougall; c) Colin Clarke

8. Kevin Keegan scored 2 FA Cup Final goals against which team?

a) Arsenal; b) Leeds United; c) Newcastle United

9. Who scored Celtic's winner in the 1967 European Cup Final?

a) Tommy Gemmell; b) Bobby Lennox; c) Steve Chalmers

Your Score	Running Total

ANSWERS

GUESS THE GUEST (Page 44): The mystery personality is swimmer Duncan Goodhew, a gold medallist at the 1980 Moscow Olympics.

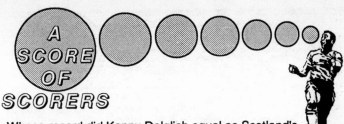

A SCORE OF SCORERS

10. Whose record did Kenny Dalglish equal as Scotland's top goalscorer in international football?
a) Hughie Gallacher; b) Jimmy McGrory; c) Denis Law

11. Who scored England's second goal in the 1966 World Cup Final at Wembley?
a) Roger Hunt; b) Martin Peters; c) Alan Ball

12. For which European country is Preben Elkjaer a star striker?
a) Denmark; b) Sweden; c) Holland

13. Against which country did Malcolm Macdonald score five goals?
a) Malta; b) Cyprus; c) Greece

14. Who has scored more League goals (434) than any other man?
a) Jackie Milburn; b) Dixie Dean; c) Arthur Rowley

15. Which player scored 23 goals in 38 internationals for Wales?
a) John Charles; b) Trevor Ford; c) Ivor Allchurch

16. Who scored Celtic's winning goal in the 1985 Scottish Cup Final?
a) Roy Aitken; b) Davie Provan; c) Frank McGarvey

17. How many League goals did John Barnes score for Watford?
a) 65; b) 75; c) 85

18. Which Irishman scored for Aston Villa in the 1957 FA Cup Final?
a) Billy Bingham; b) Pat Saward; c) Peter McParland

19. Who scored Forest's winner in the 1980 European Cup Final?
a) John Robertson; b) Gary Birtles; c) Martin O'Neill

20. The fastest World Cup finals goal was scored by which player?
a) Kevin Keegan; b) Trevor Brooking; c) Bryan Robson

ANSWERS

HOW WELL D'YOU KNOW SEBASTIAN COE? (Page 45): 1. Sheffield; 2. Loughborough; 3. His father, Peter Coe; 4. 800m, 1500m, one mile; 5. 1,000m; 6. Steve Ovett; 7. No; 8. 800 metres (1m 41.73s); 9. Brussels; 10. Steve Cram.

Your Score

Running Total

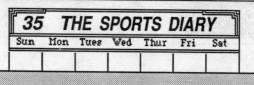

QUIZ OF THE YEAR

On the following pages we present a Quiz of the Year, recalling some of the greatest events in sporting history.
All you have to do is select the correct year for each event. Greavsie said this test put years on him!

There are 120 events listed. One point for each correct answer.
Average score: 58
Greavsie: 62

1st.: Bob Hayes sets new world record for 100 yards with 9.1 seconds clocking on New Year's Day
1960
1962
1964

2nd.: British's football's first six figure attendance for a League game watch Rangers v Celtic
1929
1939
1949

10th.: Manchester United conquer Aston Villa 6-4 in a classic third round FA Cup tie at Villa Park
1948
1950
1952

11th.: Master batsman Hanif Mohammad completes a world record innings one short of 500 runs
1956
1959
1961

14th.: Jimmy McGrory nets a Scottish League record eight goals as Celtic outclass Dunfermline
1928
1930
1932

22nd.: Joe Davis scores the first maximum 147 break in an official competitive snooker match
1950
1955
1960

23rd.: Welsh wizard Winstone stops Seki in 9 rounds to become the world nine-stone champion
1964
1966
1968

26th.: The Rugby Football Union is formed and laws are drawn up that are internationally accepted
1871
1881
1891

27th.: New Zealander Snell lowers world mile record to 3min. 54.4sec. on a grass track at Wanganui
1960
1962
1964

29th.: Alec Stock scores winning goal as Yeovil shock mighty Sunderland with a 2-1 FA Cup giantkilling
1949
1951
1953

ANSWERS

A SCORE OF SCORERS (Page 47): 10. Denis Law; 11. Martin Peters; 12, Denmark; 13. Cyprus; 14. Arthur Rowley; 15. Trevor Ford; 16. Frank McGarvey; 17. 65; 18. Peter McParland; 19. John Robertson; 20. Bryan Robson.

Your Score

Running Total

QUIZ OF THE YEAR   February

1st.: Paul 'Thunderboots' Thorburn drop-kicks a goal from 70 yards for Wales against Scotland
1984
1985
1986

3rd.: Downhill skier Toni Sailer becomes the first man to win three gold medals at one winter Olympics
1956
1960
1964

4th.: Merciless Minter knocks out Valsecchi in fifth round to win the European championship
1973
1975
1977

5th.: Non-Leaguers Hereford dump Newcastle out of the FA Cup with a startling 2-1 victory
1972
1973
1974

6th.: Taylor's superb last-minute conversion gives Wales a 19-18 victory over Scotland at Murrayfield
1973
1975
1971

11th.: Britain's John Curry skates to Olympic gold with the style of a Nureyev on ice
1972
1976
1980

12th.: Bucaneering Buchanan becomes undisputed world lightweight champion by outpointing Navarro
1969
1970
1971

13th.: Vaughton hammers five goals as England beat Ireland 13-0 in a soccer international in Belfast
1882
1872
1892

15th.: Wicketkeeper Bob Taylor snaps up world record ten catches in the Jubilee Test in Bombay
1980
1982
1984

16th.: Frazier stops Ellis in four rounds to become the undisputed world heavyweight champion
1966
1968
1970

ANSWERS

Your Score

Running Total

The answers for the QUIZ OF THE YEAR for February are on page 52

1st.: A record Rugby Union attendance of 104,000 see Scotland beat Wales 12-10 at Murrayfield
1975
1977
1979

13th.: Patterson ko's Johansson in sixth to retain the world heavyweight championship
1957
1959
1961

15th.: Two-goal Don Rogers shoots Swindon Town to shock League Cup Final victory over Arsenal
1968
1969
1970

17th.: Fitzsimmons produces his solar plexus punch to take the world title from Gentleman Jim Corbett
1900
1897
1894

18th.: Oxford set a new course record of 16min. 45sec. to beat Cambridge in the Boat Race
1984
1982
1980

24th.: Torvill and Dean notch a record 29 maximum six marks as they win the world title in Ottawa
1984
1983
1985

25th.: Sugar Ray Robinson beats Basilio to win the world middleweight title for a record fifth time
1956
1958
1960

26th.: Watkins dashes 75 yards for a late try that lifts Wales to a win over France and to the championship
1968
1966
1964

28th.: Bob Appleyard takes 4 for 7 as England send New Zealand spinning all out for 26
1955
1953
1951

31st.: Scotland's Wee Blue Devils are hailed as the Wembley Wizards as they beat England 5-1
1923
1928
1931

ANSWERS

Your Score

Running Total

2nd.: Red Rum romps home by 25 lengths to complete a glorious treble in the Grand National — 1977 / 1975 / 1976

5th.: Lloyd Honeyghan captures the vacant British welterweight title by outpointing Cliff Gilpin — 1981 / 1982 / 1983

6th.: French aristocrat Baron Pierre de Coubertin inaugurates the modern Olympics in Athens — 1886 / 1896 / 1904

15th.: Viv Richards plunders the fastest Test century off 56 balls as England bowlers toil in Antigua — 1985 / 1987 / 1986

16th.: Marvelous Marvin Hagler ko's Tommy Hearns in three rounds in world middleweight title showdown — 1983 / 1984 / 1985

17th.: A British record crowd of 149,547 see Scotland beat England 3-1 at Hampden Park — 1927 / 1937 / 1947

19th.: Bobby Charlton scores a spectacular goal in his debut for England against Scotland — 1954 / 1956 / 1958

20th.: Joe Mercer's Manchester City are victorious in Vienna in the European Winners' Cup Final — 1970 / 1969 / 1968

23rd.: Canadian cueman Cliff Thorburn scores the first maximum 147 break in a world championship match — 1985 / 1984 / 1983

24th.: Manchester United come from behind to beat Blackpool 4-2 in a classic FA Cup Final — 1948 / 1950 / 1952

Your Score / Running Total

ANSWERS

QUIZ OF THE YEAR, February (Page 50): 1st.: 1986; 3rd.: 1956; 4th.: 1977; 5th.: 1972; 6th.: 1971; 11th.: 1976; 12th: 1971; 13th: 1882; 15th.: 1980; 16th.: 1970.

5th.: A record 102,569 crowd see Warrington win the Rugby League Cup Final at the Odsal Stadium

1950
1954
1958

10th.: Dalglish scores at Wembley to clinch a second European Cup triumph for Liverpool

1978
1979
1977

11th.: Renaldo Nehemiah becomes first man to break the 13 seconds barrier in the 110 metres hurdles

1981
1980
1979

12th.: Matthews-inspired England sink Germany 6-3 and silence 110,000 crowd in Berlin

1937
1938
1939

15th.: Bradman's Aussies hammer a record 721 runs in a single day against Essex at Southend

1946
1948
1950

16th.: Ruthless Rocky Marciano stops British bulldog Don Cockell in nine rounds of savagery

1953
1954
1955

21st.: Osgood goal clinches Chelsea win over Real Madrid in European Cup Winners' Cup Final replay

1970
1971
1972

25th.: Jesse Owens sets six new world records in 45 minutes during a college meet at Michigan

1936
1935
1934

28th.: Cloughie's Forest retain the European Cup with a 1-0 win over Keegan's Hamburg

1980
1981
1982

30th.: Foster and Phillip share the wickets as Essex rush Surrey out for 14 runs in 14 overs

1982
1983
1984

ANSWERS

QUIZ OF THE YEAR, March (Page 51): 1st.: 1975; 13th.: 1961; 15th.: 1969; 17th.: 1897; 18th.: 1984; 24th.: 1984; 25th.: 1958; 26th.: 1966; 28th.: 1955; 31st.: 1928.

Your Score

Running Total

1st.: Kent bowler Colin Blythe takes 17 Northants wickets for 48 runs in one day's play
1907
1917
1927

4th.: Willie Carson wins the Oaks for the Queen on Dunfermline in Her Majesty's Jubilee year
1976
1977
1978

7th.: Renate Stecher becomes fastest woman on earth as she breaks the 11 sec. barrier in the 100 metres
1973
1976
1979

11th.: Larry Holmes stops Gerry Cooney in 13 rounds to retain his world heavyweight title in Las Vegas
1980
1982
1984

12th.: Golden Bear Nicklaus produces record round of 63 on his way to the US Open championship
1976
1978
1980

13th.: De Stefano inspires Real Madrid to victory in the first European Cup Final in Paris
1953
1956
1959

21st.: Brazil beat Italy 4-1 to win the Jules Rimet trophy outright with their third World Cup triumph
1962
1974
1970

28th.: Unbeatable hot dog Mick the Miller wins the Greyhound Derby for second successive year
1930
1932
1934

29th.: Ambling Alp Primo Carnera ko's Jack Sharkey in six rounds to win the world heavyweight title
1928
1933
1938

30th.: Lynn 'The Leap' Davies becomes the first British athlete to reach 27 feet in the long jump
1968
1966
1964

Your Score

Running Total

ANSWERS

QUIZ OF THE YEAR, April (Page 52): 2nd.: 1977; 5th.: 1983; 6th.: 1896; 15th.: 1986; 16th.: 1985; 17th.: 1937; 19th.: 1958; 20th.: 1970; 23rd.: 1983; 24th.: 1948.

1st.: Ali outpoints Bugner in breakfast-time world heavyweight title fight in Kuala Lumpur
1975
1977
1973

4th.: Jack Dempsey knocks Jess Willard down seven times in first round and wins the title in the third
1909
1919
1929

6th.: Laver takes just 52 minutes to beat Mulligan in straight sets to win his second Wimbledon title
1966
1964
1962

13th.: Uruguay conquer Argentina 4-2 to win the first World Cup Final in Montevideo
1930
1934
1938

14th.: Yorkshire spin king Hedley Verity takes 17 Essex wickets for 91 runs in one day's play
1939
1936
1933

16th.: A record crowd of 205,000 see Uruguay clinch the World Cup by beating Brazil 2-1 in Rio de Janeiro
1952
1953
1950

18th.: Jersey Joe Walcott becomes the oldest world heavyweight champ by knocking out Ezzard Charles
1951
1949
1947

19th.: Derek Ibbotson regains the world mile record for Britain with a 3min. 57.2sec. clocking
1955
1957
1959

25th.: Ed Moses wins the Olympic gold medal in the 400 metres hurdles with world record 47.63 seconds
1972
1968
1976

29th.: American long-distance swimmer Penny Dean crosses the Channel in a record 7 hours 40 minutes
1978
1975
1971

ANSWERS

QUIZ OF THE YEAR, May (Page 53): 5th.: 1954; 10th.: 1978; 11th.: 1979; 12th.: 1938; 15th.: 1948; 16th.: 1955; 21st.: 1971; 25th.: 1935; 28th.: 1980; 30th.: 1983.

Your Score

Running Total

1st.: EastEnder Ted 'Kid' Lewis outpoints Jack Britton in Boston to win the world welterweight title
1915
1920
1925

6th.: Schoolboy Bob Mathias wins the gold medal in the Olympic decathlon at the age of seventeen
1956
1952
1948

7th.: Bannister outkicks Landy in Commonwealth Games mile final as both duck under 4 minutes
1952
1954
1956

8th.: John L. Sullivan stops Jake Kilrain in 75th round of last world title fight decided with bare fists
1875
1889
1899

15th.: Surrey spinner Pat Pocock takes seven Sussex wickets in 11 deliveries at Eastbourne
1972
1975
1978

18th.: Motor racing ace Juan-Manuel Fangio drives in his final Grand Prix and clinches his fifth world title
1957
1959
1961

28th.: Australia set up their Test victory over England at The Oval that leads to the burning of the Ashes
1872
1892
1882

29th.: Twenty clubs agree to break away from the Rugby Union and to form the Rugby League
1895
1900
1905

30th.: Ian Botham completes the double of 1,000 runs and 100 wickets in a record 21 Tests
1978
1979
1977

31st.: Adrienne Beames becomes the first woman to beat the three hours barrier in the marathon
1961
1965
1969

Your Score | Running Total

ANSWERS

3rd.: 'Red Rocket' Borzov breaks the American sprint monopoly with an Olympics double
1976
1972
1968

6th.: Elliott shatters world record as he wins Olympic 1500 metres final by 20 metres from Jazy
1956
1964
1960

12th.: Arbroath slam Bon Accord 36-0 in the Scottish Cup to set a record score for British football
1885
1895
1900

13th.: Piggott captures his third St Leger as he drives Ribocco first past the post at Doncaster
1959
1963
1967

15th.: Ali regains the world heavyweight championship for a second time with revenge win over Spinks
1978
1977
1976

20th.: Billie-Jean King beats Bobby Riggs in 'Battle of the Sexes' tennis showdown in Texas
1971
1973
1975

21st.: England suffer first defeat by a visiting team when Eire win 2-0 in an international at Goodison
1939
1949
1959

23rd.: Liverpool flatten Fulham 10-0 in a second round first leg League Cup tie at Anfield
1984
1985
1986

27th.: Ezzard Charles outpoints Joe Louis to become the undisputed world heavyweight champion
1952
1951
1950

30th.: Rinty Monaghan and Terry Allen battle to a draw in all-British world flyweight title fight
1947
1949
1948

ANSWERS

QUIZ OF THE YEAR, July (Page 55): 1st.: 1975; 4th.: 1919; 6th.: 1962; 13th.: 1930; 14th.: 1933; 16th.: 1950; 18th.: 1951; 19th.: 1957; 25th.: 1976; 29th.: 1978.

Your Score

Running Total

QUIZ OF THE YEAR — October

1st.: John Conteh outpoints Ahumada at Wembley to become world light-heavyweight champion
1970
1978
1974

3rd: Sea Bird II hailed as the 'Horse of the Century' after six-length victory in the Arc de Triomphe
1965
1967
1969

5th: Gordon Richards completes his record run of 12 successive winners at Chepstow meeting
1953
1943
1933

13th.: Chataway breaks world record as he pips Kuts in a floodlit thriller at London's White City
1950
1954
1956

15th.: Proud Preston hammer Hyde 26-0 in first round to set an FA Cup goal scoring record
1887
1907
1877

18th.: Lee Evans runs 43.8 sec. for the 400 metres to set a world record that becomes a real long runner!
1966
1968
1970

20th.: Ann Packer produces a blistering finish to strike gold in the Olympic 800 metres final
1964
1960
1956

23rd.: Partick Thistle score a startling 4-1 victory over Celtic in the Scottish League Cup Final
1973
1972
1971

30th.: Ali wins the 'Rumble in the Jungle' by knocking out rope-a-doped Foreman in the eighth round
1974
1975
1976

31st.: Phil Bennett inspires Llanelli to a magnificent victory over Kirkpatrick's All Blacks
1974
1972
1973

Your Score

Running Total

ANSWERS

QUIZ OF THE YEAR, August (Page 56): 1st.: 1915; 6th.: 1948; 7th.: 1954; 8th.: 1889; 15th.: 1972; 18th.: 1957; 28th.: 1882; 29th.: 1895; 30th.: 1979; 31st.: 1971.

3rd.: Jim Watt vanquishes Vasquez in nine rounds to retain the world lightweight championship
1979
1980
1981

7th.: Carlos Monzon wins world middleweight boxing title to start a record seven year reign
1968
1970
1972

14th.: Seven Arsenal players help England beat World Cup holders Italy in the 'Battle of Highbury'
1934
1937
1930

16th.: Tottenham idol Willie Hall scores five goals for England as Ireland are outclassed at Old Trafford
1938
1946
1932

17th.: Lionel Cooper notches ten tries in one Rugby League match for Huddersfield against Keighley
1951
1954
1959

20th.: England win 8-3 in first soccer international played entirely under the Wembley floodlights
1948
1955
1958

22nd.: Fran Cotton leads North West Counties to a thrilling 16-14 victory over the All Blacks
1976
1974
1972

23rd.: Stalbridge Colonist stops an Arkle hat-trick in the Hennessy Gold Cup at Newbury
1962
1966
1968

28th.: Russia's 'Red Robot' Kuts wins the 5,000 metres to complete a golden double in the Olympics
1952
1956
1960

30th.: Floyd Patterson knocks out Archie Moore in fifth round to win the vacant world heavyweight title
1956
1957
1958

ANSWERS

QUIZ OF THE YEAR, September (Page 57): 3rd.: 1972; 6th.: 1960; 12th.: 1885; 13th.: 1967; 15th.: 1978; 20th.: 1973; 21st.: 1949; 23rd.: 1986; 27th.: 1950; 30th.: 1949.

Your Score

Running Total

QUIZ OF THE YEAR (December

1st.: Terry Spinks and Dick McTaggart strike gold for Britain in the Olympic boxing ring
1956
1960
1952

5th.: Sunderland outclass championship-chasing Newcastle United 9-1 at St James's Park
1913
1908
1905

6th.: Charlie Magri stops Dave Smith in seventh to win the British flyweight title in only his third fight
1977
1978
1976

7th.: England beat Austria's 'Wunderteam' 4-3 in a classic international at Stamford Bridge
1930
1932
1934

8th.: Carpentier 'The Orchid Man' ko's Bombardier Billy Wells in first round of European title fight
1913
1921
1919

10th.: Non-Leaguers Boston United hammer Derby 6-1 in an FA Cup tie at the Baseball Ground
1950
1955
1960

12th.: Bonecrusher Smith stops Witherspoon in first round to win WBA heavyweight championship
1986
1987
1985

14th.: Australia and West Indies complete the first tie in Test cricket history in a thriller at Brisbane
1958
1960
1962

20th.: Sugar Ray Robinson wins his first world crown when he takes the welterweight title from Tom Bell
1946
1948
1950

26th.: Graham Leggat nets four as Fulham give Ipswich a 10-1 Boxing Day hammering at Craven Cottage
1960
1963
1966

 Your Score

 Running Total

ANSWERS

QUIZ OF THE YEAR, October (Page 58): 1st.: 1974; 3rd.: 1965; 5th.: 1933; 13th.: 1954; 15th.: 1887; 18th.: 1968; 20th.: 1964; 23rd.: 1971; 30th.: 1974; 31st.: 1972.

HOW WELL D'YOU KNOW...?

JOHN BARNES

Award yourself one point for each question you can answer about footballer John Barnes
 Average score: 4 Greavsie: 7

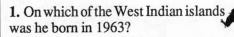

1. On which of the West Indian islands was he born in 1963?

2. With which League club did he start his career in professional football?

3. Which manager selected him for his first-team debut?

4. Against which home country did he make his England debut as a substitute in 1983?

5. Against which team did he score a spectacular solo goal for England during the 1984 South American tour?

6. He collected a runners-up medal in the 1984 FA Cup Final against which team?

7. What was the fee when Kenny Dalglish bought him for Liverpool in 1987?

8. He came on as a substitute for one game in the 1986 World Cup finals — against which team?

9. He scored two goals for England against which team in a European championship qualifying match in 1987?

10. Which number shirt did he wear regularly during Liverpool's 1987-88 championship season?

ANSWERS

QUIZ OF THE YEAR, November (Page 59): 3rd.: 1979; 7th.: 1970; 14th.: 1934; 16th,: 1938; 17th.: 1951: 20th.: 1963; 22nd.: 1972; 23rd.: 1966; 28th. 1956; 30th.: 1956.

Your Score *Running Total*

37 THE NAME GAME

EACH clue leads to a well-known name. Put the initials in the appropriate squares to identify a 'golden oldie' sports star: Two points for each correct answer, plus a bonus of ten points for completing the main name.

Average score: 10 Greavsie: 18

1	2	3	4	5	6	
7	8	9	10	11	12	13

10 & 2	This Irishman has been a Goliath at the heart of Arsenal's defence for a decade.
8 & 11	The Brockton Blockbuster who won all of his 49 professional fights.
12 & 4	He beat Jimmy Connors to become the Wimbledon singles champion in 1975.
9 & 6	The man who has been in the corner with Muhammad Ali and Sugar Ray Leonard.
13	Paavo, the Flying Finn who ran away with nine Olympic gold medals.
1 & 5	He remains Australia's leading taker of wickets in Test cricket.
3 & 7	The explosive West Ham middleweight known as the Dark Destroyer.

Your Score	Running Total

ANSWERS

QUIZ OF THE YEAR (Page 60): 1st.: 1956; 5th.: 1908; 6th.: 1977; 7th.: 1932; 8th.: 1913; 10th.: 1955; 12th.: 1986; 14th.: 1960; 20th.: 1946; 26th.: 1963.

You have five minutes to answer each teaser.
You get two points for each correct answer and
a 5-point bonus each time you beat the clock.

38 BEAT THE CLOCK

Average score: 48 Greavsie: 50

1. Name the six clubs that were runners-up in FA Cup Finals during the 1970s.

2. Name the eight Derby winners from 1975 to 1982.

3. Name the nine British heavyweight boxers who have held the European title since the war.

4. Name the ten sprinters who have won the gold medal in the men's 100 metres in post-war Olympic Games.

5. Name the seven men who have managed Liverpool since the war.

ANSWERS

HOW WELL D'YOU KNOW JOHN BARNES? 1. Jamaica; 2. Watford; 3.
Graham Taylor; 4. Northern Ireland; 5. Brazil; 6. Everton; 7. £900,000; 8.
Argentina; 9. Turkey; 10. No. 10.

Your
Score

Running
Total

WHO'S WHO OF THE OLYMPICS

Here are 15 questions that will provide you with a Who's Who test of your knowledge of Olympic champions. One point for each correct answer.
Average score: 6
Greavsie: 8

1. Who set a world record on the track in the women's 400 metres in the Montreal Games of 1976?
a) Irena Szewinska; b) Marita Koch; c) Jarmila Kratochvilova

2. Who won two successive gold medals for Britain in the middle-weight boxing division?
a) Chris Finnegan; b) Harry Mallin; c) Johnny Douglas

3. Who won four gold medals and a silver on the track in the men's Olympics of 1948 and 1952?
a) Emil Zatopek; b) Harrison Dillard; c) Gaston Reiff

4. Who was the second boxer to win three Olympic gold medals?
a) Jerzy Kulej; b) Angel Herrara; c) Teofilio Stevenson

5. Who was the first cyclist to win three Olympic gold medals?
a) Daniel Morelon; b) Paul Masson; c) Robert Carpentier

6. Who is the only equestrian rider to have won the individual gold medal twice in the Olympic grand prix?
a) Pierre d'Oriola; b) Hans-Gunter Winkler; c) Raimondo d'Inzeo

7. Who was the first figure skater to win three gold medals?
a) Gillis Grafstrom; b) Sonja Henie; c) Dick Button

ANSWERS

Your Score

Running Total

THE NAME GAME (Page 59): DONALD BRADMAN (David O'Leary, Rocky Marciano, Arthur Ashe, Angelo Dundee, (Paavo) Nurmi, Dennis Lillee, Nigel Benn).

8. Who was the athlete who won four gold medals on the track in the men's athletics in the Munich and Montreal Olympics?
a) Valeri Borzov; b) Lasse Viren; c) Miruts Yifter

9. Who was the first men's Alpine skier to win three gold medals?
a) Toni Sailer; b) Franz Klammer; c) Jean-Claude Killy

10. Who won four gold medals in the pool in the 1964 Olympic swimming championships?
a) Mark Spitz; b) Don Schollander; c) Jon Konrads

11. Who was the British boxer voted the outstanding stylist in the 1956 Olympic finals in Melbourne?
a) Terry Spinks; b) Nicky Gargano; c) Dick McTaggart

12. Who is the athlete who won a record 10 gold medals in the standing jump events?
a) Ray Ewry; b) James Connolly; c) Alvin Kraenzlein

13. Who is the sculler who won three individual gold medals in the Games of 1956, 1960 and 1964?
a) John Kelly; b) Stuart Makenzie; c) Vyacheslav Ivanov

14. Who won three gold medals on the track in the 1956 Olympics and added a fourth to her collection in 1964?
a) Shirley Strickland; b) Betty Cuthbert; c) Wilma Rudolph

15. Who is the weightlifter who won a record four medals in the Olympics of 1952, 1956, 1960 and 1964?
a) Norbert Schemansky; b) John Davis; c) Vasili Alexeyev

ANSWERS

BEAT THE CLOCK (Page 63): 1. Leeds (1970-73); Liverpool (1971-77), Arsenal (1972-78), Newcastle (1974), Fulham (1975), Manchester United (1976-79). 2. Grundy (1975), Empery (1976), The Minstrel (1977), Shirley Heights (1978), Troy (1979), Henbit (1980), Shergar (1981), Golden Fleece (1982). 3. Bruce Woodcock, Jack Gardner, Dick Richardson, Henry Cooper, Joe Bugner, Jack Bodell, Richard Dunn, John L. Gardner, Frank Bruno. 4. Harrison Dillard, Lindy Remigino, Bobby-Joe Morrow, Armin Hary, Bob Hayes, Jim Hines, Valeriy Borzov, Hasely Crawford, Allan Wells, Carl Lewis. 5. George Kay, Don Welsh, Phil Taylor, Bill Shankly, Bob Paisley, Joe Fagan, Kenny Dalglish.

BJORN WINNERS

Bjorn Borg was arguably the greatest of all Wimbledon champions. What do you recall of his five winning finals? Award yourself two points for each of the questions that you answer correctly.
Average score: 4 Greavsie: 8

1976: How old was Borg when he won his first singles final on the Centre Court at Wimbledon?

a) 20; b) 21; c) 19

1977: Who was his opponent when he won his second championship 3-6, 6-2, 6-1, 5-7, 6-4 in a three-and-a-half hour marathon?

a) Ilie Nastase; b) Jimmy Connors; c) Stan Smith

1978: In how many sets did he win his third championship to equal Fred Perry's feat?

a) five sets; b) four sets; c) straight sets

1979: Who was Borg's opponent when he won his fourth successive championship to set a new record?

a) Roscoe Tanner; b) Vitas Gerulaitis; c) Arthur Ashe

1980: The player he beat for his fifth championship was the man who the following year ended his incredible reign as king of Wimbledon. Who was it?

a) Ivan Lendl; b) Pat Cash; c) John McEnroe

ANSWERS

Your Score

Running Total

WHO'S WHO OF THE OLYMPICS (Page 64): 1. Irena Szewinska; 2. Harry Mallin; 3. Emil Zatopek; 4. Teofilio Stevenson; 5. Paul Masson; 6. Pierre d'Oriola; 7. Gillis Grafstrom.

41 THE FIVE STAR TEST

Award yourself one point for each correct identification in this five-star test.

Average score: 11 Greavsie: 16

1. Which five of these boxers won Olympic gold medals?—Pascual Perez, Mike Tyson, Leon Spinks, Don Curry, Ray Leonard, Hector Camacho, Marvin Hagler, Mate Parlov, Mark Breland, Eusebio Pedroza.

2. Which five of these managers have never been in charge of a League championship-winning team?—Ron Greenwood, Arthur Rowe, Harry Catterick, John Bond, Ron Saunders, Bobby Robson, Dave Sexton, Bertie Mee, Brian Clough, Ron Atkinson.

3. Which five of these batsmen scored more than one hundred 100s during their career?—Geoff Boycott, Tom Graveney, Bill Edrich, Dennis Amiss, Peter May, Ken Barrington, John Edrich, Cyril Washbrook, Colin Cowdrey, M.J.K. (Mike) Smith.

4. Which five of these golfers have won the world matchplay championship?—Greg Norman, Bill Rogers, Ben Crenshaw, Peter Thomson, Arnold Palmer, Lee Trevino, Tom Weiskopf, Neil Coles, Raymond Floyd, Bob Charles.

5. Which five of these post-war tennis players never won a Wimbledon singles title?—Christine Truman, Shirley Fry, Doris Hart, Angela Buxton, Rosie Casals, Margaret Osborne, Nancy Richy, Pauline Betz, Karen Susman, Judy Tegart.

ANSWERS

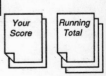

Your Score | Running Total

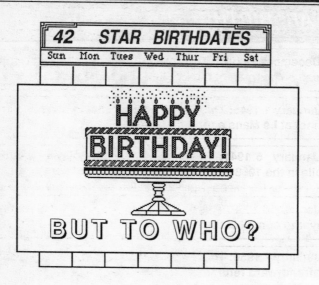

42 STAR BIRTHDATES

Sun	Mon	Tues	Wed	Thur	Fri	Sat

On the following pages we present the birthdates and star signs of 120 famous sports personalities of the past and present. Award yourself one point for each one that you can identify.

Average score: 53
Greavsie: 57

STAR BIRTHDATES · Capricorn

1. December 31 1929: This former Surrey and England captain became chairman of the England Test selectors.

2. January 1 1945: This Belgian motor racing ace has been a winner at Le Mans a record six times.

3. January 5 1941: This American tennis player beat Fred Stolle in the 1963 men's Wimbledon singles final.

4. January 6 1959: This Indian all-rounder was the youngest player to complete the double of 1,000 wickets and 100 runs.

5. January 7 1950: This former Fulham, Luton and Newcastle centre-forward returned to management in 1987.

6. January 12 1944: This boxer was world heavyweight champion until walking into George Foreman's fists in Jamaica.

7. January 14 1948: This Australian golfer has a brother who was one of the world's great wicket-keepers.

8. January 16 1948: This snooker player was knocked out of the 1988 world championship semi-finals by Steve Davis.

9. January 17 1926: This great West Indian batsman was one of 'The Three Ws' and doubled as a wicket-keeper.

10. January 18 1921: This Doncaster-based boxer was Britain's first post-war heavyweight champion.

ANSWERS

FIVE STAR TEST: 1. Pascual Perez, Leon Spinks, Ray Leonard, Mate Parlov, Mark Breland; 2. Ron Greenwood, John Bond, Bobby Robson, Dave Sexton, Ron Atkinson; 3. Geoff Boycott, Tom Graveney, Dennis Amiss, John Edrich, Colin Cowdrey; 4. Greg Norman, Bill Rogers, Arnold Palmer, Tom Weiskopf, Bob Charles; 5. Christine Truman, Angela Buxton, Rosie Casals, Nancy Richy, Judy Tegart.

Your Score

Running Total

1. January 22 1920: This former Southampton, Spurs and England full-back later managed Ipswich and England.

2. January 26 1907: This golfer won the British Open three times and he had a ball named after his famous round of 65.

3. January 29 1926: This American tennis player beat John Bromwich in the 1948 men's Wimbledon singles final.

4. February 3 1936: This former Australian Test captain was recognised as one of the greatest of all slip fielders.

5. February 6 1924: This former Wolves and England captain managed Arsenal before becoming a television executive.

6. February 9 1958: This golfer was British Open champion in 1985 and US Masters winner in 1988.

7. February 10 1926: This footballer captained Northern Ireland in the 1958 World Cup and Spurs in their double year.

8. February 11 1909: This boxer took the world heavyweight title from Primo Carnera and lost it to James J. Braddock.

9. February 15 1929: This British driver won two world titles and started in a record 176 Grand Prix events.

10. February 18 1957: This outstanding East German athlete won the women's 400 metres in the 1980 Olympics.

ANSWERS

Your Score

Running Total

The Aquarius Star Birthday answers are on page 72.

STAR BIRTHDATES Pisces

1. **February 20 1947:** This England centre-forward won FA Cup winners' medals with Chelsea and Southampton.

2. **February 22 1907:** This England centre-forward scored a record 60 First Division goals in one season for Everton.

3. **February 24 1955:** This French driver was world champion in 1987 and has won a record total of Grand Prix races.

4. **February 26 1946:** This former Manchester City and England midfield player was nicknamed Nijinsky.

5. **March 7 1960:** This Czech-born tennis star won his first top title when he beat John McEnroe in the 1984 French final.

6. **March 9 1952:** This Fylde lock forward captained England's Rugby Union team for a record stretch of 21 games.

7. **March 13 1950:** This boxer was born in Hungary and twice went the distance with Muhammad Ali.

8. **March 14 1956:** This athlete was born in Jamaica and won the gold medal in the 1984 women's javelin.

9. **March 17 1957:** This ice skater won the gold medal for Britain in the men's figure skating event at the 1980 Olympics.

10. **March 18 1956:** This Swedish skier won a record 14 World Cup events during the 1979 season.

ANSWERS

STAR BIRTHDATES, Capricorn (Page 69): 1. Peter May; 2. Jackie Ickx; 3. Chuck McKinley; 4. Kapil Dev; 5. Malcolm Macdonald; 6. Joe Frazier; 7. Graham Marsh; 8. Cliff Thorburn; 9. Clyde Walcott; 10. Bruce Woodcock.

Your Score

Running Total

STAR BIRTHDATES — Aries

1. **March 21 1935:** This Sunderland and Middlesbrough centre-forward started his managerial career with Hartlepool.

2. **March 23 1952:** This Cuban heavyweight boxer won the first of his Olympic gold medals at Munich in 1972.

3. **April 2 1926:** This Australian was knighted after three times winning the world motor drivers' championship.

4. **April 5 1945:** This Liverpool defender was captain at Anfield where he was famed and feared for his ferocious tackling.

5. **April 9 1946:** He followed Godfrey Evans as wicket-keeper for Kent and England.

6. **April 10 1960:** This sprinter clocked a British record 10.04 seconds for the 100 metres in Madrid in 1986.

7. **April 11 1931:** This Welsh full back scored a record 496 points for Leeds in the 1956-57 Rugby League season.

8. **April 13 1952:** This Irishman won a record 149 winners in the 1977-78 national hunt season.

9. **April 15 1939:** This Welsh boxer was the world featherweight champion until meeting Mexican Vicente Saldivar.

10. **April 19 1956:** This Torquay-born tennis player followed Virginia Wade as Britain's No 1 women's tennis player.

Your Score

Running Total

ANSWERS

1. May 1 1929: This West Indian spin bowler and his partner Alf Valentine had England's batsmen tied in knots.

2. May 2 1962: This Cockney snooker star beat Stephen Hendry in a classic contest in the 1988 world championship.

3. May 3 1934: This boxer became British heavyweight champion for the first time when outpointing Brian London in 1959.

4. May 5 1904: This flat race jockey was first past the post in a record 4870 races between 1920 and 1954.

5. May 6 1953: This footballer captained Liverpool and played in Italy before becoming a player-manager.

6. May 8 1935: This England centre-half played 629 League games for Leeds before switching to management.

7. May 10 1966: This Spanish tennis idol beat Dennis Ralston in the 1966 men's Wimbledon singles final.

8. May 12 1937: This women's road cyclist won 25 British time trial championships and was first in 71 individual road races.

9. May 18 1942: This footballer wore the number six shirt in Manchester United's 1968 European Cup winning team.

10. May 20 1942: This athlete leapt to the gold medal in the 1964 men's Olympic long jump final.

ANSWERS

STAR BIRTHDATES, Pisces (Page 71): 1. Peter Osgood; 2. Dixie Dean; 3. Alain Prost; 4. Colin Bell; 5. Ivan Lendl; 6. Billy Beaumont; 7. Joe Bugner; 8. Tessa Sanderson; 9. Robin Cousins; 10. Ingemar Stenmark.

STAR BIRTHDATES   Gemini

1. May 22 1946: This Irishman played at Old Trafford before having spells with Fulham and in the United States.

2. May 23 1954: This boxer was world middleweight champion from 1980 until Sugar Ray Leonard made a comeback.

3. May 26 1966: This athlete was born in South Africa and ran into controversy when obtaining a British passport.

4. May 27 1965: This tennis player became the first Australian to win the men's singles title at Wimbledon since 1971.

5. June 6 1940: This Irish forward captained the British Lions on their triumphant tour of South Africa in 1974.

6. June 8 1932: This Yorkshire-born spin bowler captained England and Leicestershire.

7. June 11 1939: This Scottish driver was world motor racing champion three times and had 27 Grand Prix victories.

8. June 13 1955: This Scottish football international captained Liverpool in their outstanding 1987-88 season.

9. June 16 1942: This Italian motorcycling ace won a record 15 world championships.

10. June 17 1945: This Belgian cycling champion won the Tour de France five times between 1969 and 1974.

Your Score

Running Total

ANSWERS

STAR BIRTHDATES　　Cancer

1. **June 24 1911:** This motor racing ace won the world drivers' championship a record five times.

2. **June 28 1945:** This boxer from Edinburgh was world light-weight champion until defeat at the hands of Roberto Duran.

3. **June 30 1933:** This bespectacled batsman was captain of England and also played international rugby.

4. **July 4 1918:** This Surrey bowler took 236 Test wickets and later became a top administrator.

5. **July 7 1944:** This golfer held both the British and US Open titles and has guided two winning Ryder Cup teams.

6. **July 10 1943:** This tennis player was the first black men's singles champion at Wimbledon.

7. **July 13 1944:** This footballer was a left back with Middlesbrough and Spurs before managing Torquay United.

8. **July 16 1942:** This long-time Wimbledon favourite first courted fame as Miss Smith.

9. **July 18 1944:** This athlete was a Boston University student when he struck gold for Britain in the 1968 Olympics.

10. **July 20 1938:** This footballer scored more League goals for Liverpool than any other player.

ANSWERS

STAR BIRTHDATES, Taurus (Page 73): 1. Sonny Ramadhin; 2. Jimmy White; 3. Henry Cooper; 4. Gordon Richards; 5. Graeme Souness; 6. Jack Charlton; 7. Manuel Santana; 8. Beryl Burton; 9. Nobby Stiles; 10. Lynn Davies.

Your
Score

Running
Total

STAR BIRTHDATES

Leo

1. **July 26 1936:** This football manager was in charge of the 1976 FA Cup winners and later had a spell at Roker Park.

2. **July 27 1958:** This ice skater and former policeman found fame at the double dancing to Ravel's Balero.

3. **July 28 1936:** This cricketing all-rounder was knighted by the Queen in his native Barbados.

4. **July 29 1952:** This snooker player wore 'lucky' shoes when winning the world title in his native Yorkshire in 1986.

5. **Juy 30 1958:** This all-round athlete finished 18th in his first Olympic decathlon competition in 1976.

6. **July 31 1946:** This goalscorer played for Walsall, Fulham Leicester and Leeds and later managed Leeds and Barnsley.

7. **August 9 1938:** This tennis player from Rockhampton won two Grand Slams and four Wimbledon singles titles.

8. **August 10 1948:** This Mexican boxer took the world welterweight title from Britain's John H. Stracey.

9. **August 16 1950:** This Australian cricketer was Dennis Lillee's ferociously fast bowling partner.

10. **August 1946:** This Rumanian tennis star was the temperamental but gifted clown prince of the courts.

Your Score   Running Total

ANSWERS

STAR BIRTHDATES, Gemini (Page 74): 1. George Best; 2. Marvin Hagler; 3. Zola Budd; 4. Pat Cash; 5. Willie-John McBride; 6. Ray Illingworth; 7. Jackie Stewart; 8. Alan Hansen; 9. Giacomo Agostini; 10. Eddie Merckx.

STAR BIRTHDATES — Virgo

1. August 22 1892: This England and Surrey cricketer scored a century in 35 minutes at Northampton in 1920.

2. August 27 1925: This England and Bolton centre-forward was nicknamed the Lion of Vienna.

3. August 30 1943: This idolised French skier won three gold medals at the 1968 Winter Olympics.

4. August 31 1955: This athlete has proved himself totally supreme in the 400 metres hurdles event.

5. September 4 1935: This footballer made a late League debut and captained Manchester City's 1969 FA Cup winners.

6. September 11 1950: This British motor cycling ace always had lucky 7 as his number and was a world 500cc champion.

7. September 12 1949: This Russian ice skater won a record ten world titles with two different partners.

8. September 16 1951: This Scottish Rugby star won 51 caps and was one of the greatest of all attacking full backs.

9. September 18 1949: This goalkeeper was the last line of defence in two European Cup Finals for Nottingham Forest.

10. September 19 1936: This American athlete won the gold medal in the discus in four successive Olympics.

ANSWERS

STAR BIRTHDATES, Cancer (Page 75): 1. Juan-Manuel Fangio; 2. Ken Buchanan; 3. Mike Smith; 4. Alec Beder; 5. Tony Jacklin; 6. Arthur Ashe; 7. Cyril Knowles; 8. Margaret Court; 9. David Hemery; 10. Roger Hunt.

Your Score

Running Total

1. **September 27 1941:** This goalkeeper played for Chelsea and England and was nicknamed 'The Cat.'

2. **September 29 1933:** This Rangers football idol also played for Sunderland and Forest and was nicknamed 'Slim Jim.'

3. **October 2 1948:** This West Ham United midfield player was capped 47 times by England.

4. **October 3 1933:** This Australian tennis player defeated Rod Laver in the 1960 men's singles final at Wimbledon.

5. **October 4 1939:** This New Zealand speedway ace won six world titles between 1968 and 1979.

6. **October 6 1930:** This Australian leg spinner and former Test captain once hit 11 sixes in an innings at Scarborough.

7. **October 10 1935:** This southpaw boxer from Kent twice challenged Joe Brown for the world lightweight title.

8. **October 11 1939:** This tennis player was the women's singles champion at Wimbledon in 1959, 1960 and 1964.

9. **October 13 1942:** This wee Scot won the world flyweight championship by beating Salvatore Burruni in 1966.

10. **October 17 1934:** This Fulham inside-forward captained England in the 1962 World Cup finals.

Your Score

Running Total

ANSWERS

STAR BIRTHDATES, Leo (Page 76): 1. Lawrie McMenemy; 2. Christopher Dean; 3. Garfield Sobers; 4. Joe Johnson; 5. Daley Thompson; 6. Allan Clarke; 7. Rod Laver; 8. Carlos Palomino; 9. Jeff Thomson; 10. Ilie Nastase.

STAR BIRTHDATES   Scorpio

1. October 24 1930: This Surrey and England batting master scored 256 against Australia in the 1964 Old Trafford Test.

2. October 25 1934: This jockey was champion in 1979 and won 17 of 18 races on Brigadier Gerard.

3. November 2 1960: This Algerian athlete was the Olympic 5,000 metres gold medallist in Los Angeles in 1984.

4. November 3 1949: This boxer was unbeaten world heavyweight champion until two defeats by Michael Spinks.

5. November 8 1943: This footballer played for West Ham, Spurs and Norwich and was in the 1966 World Cup team.

6. November 9 1942: This American golfer won the British Open championship at Troon in 1973.

7. November 11 1921: This footballer played for Brentford, Chelsea and Fulham and managed West Ham and England.

8. November 14 1934: This Scot played for Tottenham's double-winning team before joining Brian Clough at Derby.

9. November 17 1930: This American was the first athlete to win two successive Olympic gold medals in the decathlon.

10. November 20 1943: This tennis player won a record 20 championships at Wimbledon.

ANSWERS

STAR BIRTHDATES, Virgo (Page 77): 1. Percy Fender; 2. Nat Lofthouse; 3. Jean-Claude Killy; 4. Ed Moses; 5. Tony Book; 6. Barry Sheene; 7. Irina Rodnina; 8. Andy Irvine; 9. Peter Shilton; 10. Al Oerter.

Your Score

Running Total

STAR BIRTHDATES Sagittarius

1. **November 24 1962:** This long-kicking full back scored a record 52 points for Wales in the 1986 Rugby Union season.

2. **November 25 1952:** This idolised Pakistani all-rounder scored a century and took 11 wickets against India in 1983.

3. **November 26 1963:** This Rugby League utility back signed for Wigan from Widnes for £100,000 in 1986.

4. **December 3 1942:** This Irish fly-half and centre won a record 69 caps for Ireland between 1964 and 1979.

5. **December 4 1938:** This British rider won an individual gold medal and shared in two team titles in Olympic 3-day events.

6. **December 9 1942:** This footballer captained Leeds and Scotland and later became the boss at Elland Road.

7. **December 10 1963:** This Pakistani squash player was world champion and unbeatable from 1981 to 1985.

8. **December 12 1912:** This boxer was first to hold three world titles at the same time and was nicknamed Homicide Hank.

9. **December 13 1952:** This National Hunt jockey won a career record 1138 races from 1970 to 1985.

10. **December 21 1913:** This footballer captained Sunderland in the 1937 FA Cup Final and was named after Horatio Nelson.

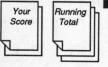

Your Score   Running Total

ANSWERS

43

Just answer 'yes' or 'no' to these football questions. One point for each correct answer and a bonus of one each time you get three right in succession.

Average score: 10 Greavsie: 14

1. Did Brian Clough play League football for Newcastle?
YES/NO

2. Was Ian Rush ever on Cardiff City's books?
YES/NO

3. Can an outfield player score direct from a goal kick?
YES/NO

4. Has Bryan Robson won more England caps than Emyln Hughes?
YES/NO

5. Do Dundee United play their home games at Dens Park?
YES/NO

6. Did George Best win an FA Cup winner's medal with Manchester United?
YES/NO

7. Did Peter Reid start his playing career with Bolton Wanderers?
YES/NO

8. Were the 1970 World Cup finals staged in Argentina?
YES/NO

9. Do Coventry City play their home games at Lowfield Road Stadium?
YES/NO

10. Did Tom Finney ever score a goal in an FA Cup Final?
YES/NO

11. Have Newcastle United had a home ground other than St James' Park?
YES/NO

12. Was George Graham capped by Scotland during his playing career?
YES/NO

13. Did West Ham goalkeeper Phil Parkes ever play for Walsall?
YES/NO

14. Has Neville Southall won more Welsh caps than Jack Kelsey?
YES/NO

15. Did Gordon Strachan score for Scotland in the 1986 World Cup finals?
YES/NO

ANSWERS

STAR BIRTHDATES, Scorpio (Page 79): 1. Ken Barrington; 2. Joe Mercer; 3. Said Aoutia; 4. Larry Holmes; 5. Martin Peters; 6. Tom Weiskopf; 7. Ron Greenwood; 8. Dave Mackay; 9. Bob Mathias; 10. Billie-Jean King.

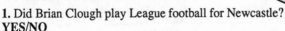

Your Score

Running Total

44

Jack
Dempsey
See question 3

GOLDIES

Each question relates to great sports champions of the past. All of them have been retired for 25 years or more. Two points for each correct answer.
Average score: 10
Greavsie: 14

1. Walter Hammond was one of the great cricketing all-rounders. With which County was he an established favourite?

a) Worcestershire; b) Gloucestershire; c) Essex

2. In which year did Gordon Richards ride his only Derby winner?

a) 1951; b) 1953; c) 1955

3. Who was Jack Dempsey's opponent in the fight that drew the first $million gate?

a) Georges Carpentier; b) Gene Tunney; c) Jess Willard

4. Arthur Wint represented which country when winning the gold medal in the 400 metres and the silver in the 800 metres in the 1948 London Olympics?

a) Great Britain; b) Tonga; c) Jamaica

5. Joe Mercer captained which winning team in an FA Cup Final at Wembley?

a) Everton; b) Manchester City; c) Arsenal

6. Who was Joe Davis's opponent when he last won the world snooker championship?

a) Horace Lindrum; b) Fred Davis; c) John Pulman

Your Score

Running Total

ANSWERS

STAR BIRTHDATES, Sagittarius (Page 80): 1 Paul Thorburn; 2. Imran Khan; 3. Joe Lydon; 4. Mike Gibson; 5. Richard Meade; 6. Billy Bremner; 7. Jahangir Khan; 8. Henry Armstrong; 9. Johnny Francome; 10. Raich Carter.

82

7. Who did Jaroslav Drobny beat in the 1954 Wimbledon men's singles final?

a) Ashley Cooper; b) Kurt Nielsen;

c) Ken Rosewall

8. How many times did American golf master Bobby Jones win the British Open?

a) Two times; b) Three times;

c) Four times

9. Who finished second to Roger Bannister when he became the first athlete to break the four minute mile barrier in 1954?

a) Chris Brasher; b) Chris Chataway; c) Bill Nankeville

Roger
Bannister
See question 9

10. In which year did Britain's Mike Hawthorn win the world motor racing drivers' championship?

a) 1954; b) 1956; c) 1958

11. Rugby League star Jim Sullivan played an all-time record 769 matches for which club between 1921 and 1946?

a) Widnes; b) Warrington; c) Wigan

12. John Charles became an idolised player with which Italian club when first sold by Leeds United?

a) Juventus; b) Inter-Milan; c) Lazio

13. In which country did Denis Compton score the fastest triple century of all time in just 181 minutes in 1948?

a) India; b) South Africa; c) New Zealand

14. Against which opponent did Rocky Marciano make the final defence of his world heavyweight championship?

a) Don Cockell; b) Ezzard Charles; c) Archie Moore

ANSWERS

Your Score

Running Total

45 MORE ODD ONES OUT

Who is the odd one out in each of the following six lists? We give you a little 'think hint' to help. Award yourself two points for each correct answer.

Average score: 4 Greavsie: 6

1. England cricketers Godfrey Evans, Bob Taylor, John Murray, Alan Knott, David Larter, Jim Parks, Keith Andrew, Arthur McIntyre. *Think wicket-keepers.*

2. British boxers Randolph Turpin, Alan Minter, Charlie Magri, Chris Finnegan, Terry Downes, Jim Watt, Lloyd Honeyghan, Terry Marsh. *Think world titles.*

3. Olympic champions Olga Korbut, Nadia Comaneci, Tatyan Kazankina, Larissa Latynina, Vera Caslavska, Nelli Kim, Karin Janz, Maxi Gnauck. *Think gymnastics.*

4. England footballers Terry Cooper, Kenny Sansom, Cyril Knowles, Ray Wilson, Paul Reaney, Stuart Pearce, Bob McNab, Gerry Byrne. *Think left-backs.*

5. Motor racing drivers Stirling Moss, Mike Hawthorn, Graham Hill, Jim Clark, John Surtees, Jackie Stewart, James Hunt. *Think world championships.*

6. American sportsmen Dan Marino, Art Monk, Hank Aaron, John Riggins, Walter Payton, William Perry, Eric Dickerson, Jim Brown. *Think of a different-shaped ball.*

ANSWERS

Your Score

Running Total

GOLDEN OLDIES (Page 82): 1. Gloucestershire; 2. 1953 (on Pinza); 3. Georges Carpentier; 4. Jamaica; 5. Arsenal; 6. Horace Lindrum.

FRANK BRUNO

Award yourself one point for each question you can answer about boxer Frank Bruno
Average score: 5 Greavsie: 6

1. Where in London was he born in 1962?

2. How old was he when he won the ABA heavyweight championship?

3. To which South American country did he go in 1981 for an eye operation that saved his boxing career?

4. With which manager did he turn professional?

5. How many professional fights did he win before his first defeat at Wembley Arena in 1984?

6. In which round was he ko'd by Bonecrusher Smith?

7. From whom did he take the European title in 1985?

8. Who did he beat in one round of a world title eliminator?

9. In which round was he stopped by Tim Witherspoon in their world title fight at Wembley in 1986?

10. At which London venue did he beat 'Aussie Joe' Bugner in a non-title fight in 1987?

ANSWERS

GOLDEN OLDIES (Page 83): 7. Ken Rosewall; 8. Three times; 9. Chris Chataway; 10. 1958; 11. Wigan; 12. Juventus; 13. South Africa; 14. Archie Moore.

Your Score

Running Total

Do you know your way around the sports world? This will test you. One point each time you know where you are. **Average score: 6 Greavsie: 7**

Where are you when you're watching...

1. League football at Upton Park

2. Test cricket at Edgbaston

3. The King George V1 & Queen Elizabeth Diamond Stakes

4. A motor racing Grand Prix at the Zolder circuit

5. World championship boxing at Caesars Palace Hotel

6. A golf tournament in Roberto de Vicenzo's home country

7. Athletics in the stadium built for the 1976 Olympics

8. A Rugby Union international at Eden Park

9. The Redskins playing in a home American football match

10. The Pistons in a home basketball match

11. Dutch League football at Feyenoord's home ground

12. A cricket match in the land of Ted Dexter's birth

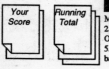

Your Score   Running Total

ANSWERS

MORE ODD ONES OUT: 1. David Larter (was a bowler not a wicket-keeper); 2. Chris Finnegan (did not win a world title); 3. Tatyana Kazankina (was an Olympic champion athlete, not a gymnast); 4. Paul Reaney (was a right-back); 5. Stirling Moss (did not win a world championship); 6. Hank Aaron (was a baseball star).

JUMP TO IT!

Take a trip round the 30 jumps on the Grand National course at Aintree in a hunt for a possible 100 points. The all-sports questions become harder the more difficult the jumps.

Average score: 58
Greavsie: 62

Fence No 1: Thorn fence, 4ft 6in high; dressed with gorse.
Points value: Two

What is the distance of the Grand National Course at Aintree?
a) 5 miles 865 yards; b) 4 miles 865 yards; c) 3 miles 865 yards

Fence No 2: Thorn fence, 4ft 7in high; dressed with gorse.
Points value: Two

Which world heavyweight boxing champion twice defeated Roland LaStarza?
a) Rocky Marciano; b) Jess Willard; c) Ezzard Charles

Fence No 3: Open Ditch, ditch 6ft, fence 5ft; dressed with spruce
Points value: Three

Who rode Grittar to victory at 7-1 in the 1982 Grand National?
a) Bob Davies; b) Dick Saunders; c) Peter Scudamore

Fence No 4: Thorn fence, 4ft 10in high; dressed with fir
Points value: Two

Who netted two goals in England's 1966 World Cup semi-final?
a) Martin Peters; b) Bobby Charlton; c) Roger Hunt

ANSWERS

Your Score

Running Total

Fence No 5: Thorn fence, 4ft 10in high; dressed with fir.
Points value: Two

Which batsman averaged 102.53 for the 1979 County season?
a) Geoff Boycott; b) Dennis Amiss; c) John Edrich

 Fence No 6: Becher's Brook. 4ft 10in high fence followed by 5ft 6in brook
Points value: Five

On which horse did Pat Taafe win the 1970 Grand National?
a) Specify; b) Highland Wedding; c) Gay Trip

 Fence No 7: Thorn fence, 4ft 6in high; dressed with fir
Points value: Two

Which club did Gothenburg beat in the 1987 UEFA Cup Final?
a) Aberdeen; b) Dundee United; c) Hearts

 Fence No 8: Canal Turn, fence 5ft high; dressed with fir
Points value: Five

What were the odds of 1985 Grand National winner Last Suspect?
a) 66-1; b) 33-1; c) 50-1

 Fence No 9: Valentine's Brook, 5ft thorn fence followed by 5ft 6in brook
Points value: Three

Which horse won the National in successive years in 1935, 1936?
a) Golden Miller; b) Reynoldstown; c) Royal Mail

 Fence No 10: Thorn fence, 5ft high; dressed with fir
Points value: Two

Which County did Notts beat in the 1987 NatWest Trophy final?
a) Northants; b) Kent; c) Lancashire

Your Score | Running Total

ANSWERS

GOING PLACES (Page 86): 1. West Ham United; 2. Birmingham; 3. Ascot; 4. Belgium; 5. Las Vegas; 6. Argentina; 7. Montreal; 8. Auckland, New Zealand; 9. Washington; 10. Detroit; 11. Rotterdam; 12. Italy.

Fence No 11: Open ditch, 6ft ditch followed by 5ft thorn fence dressed with fir.
Points value: Three

With which sport do you associate the name Scott Hamilton?
a) Ice skating; b) Cycling; c) Gymnastics

Fence No 12: 5ft thorn fence followed by a ditch 5ft 6in wide
Points value: Three

Who hit 21 sixes in the 1986 John Player League?
a) Allan Lamb; b) Graham Gooch; c) Ian Botham

Fence No 13: Thorn fence, 4ft 7in high; dressed with gorse
Points value: Two

Against which opponent did Muhammad Ali have his last fight?
a) Larry Holmes; b) Trevor Berbick; c) Leon Spinks

Fence No 14: Thorn fence, 4ft 6in high; dressed with fir
Points value: Two

Which Third Division club reached the FA Cup semi-final in 1984?
a) Plymouth; b) Walsall; c) Notts County

Fence No 15: The Chair, an open 6ft ditch followed by a 5ft 2in high thorn fence
Points value: Seven

Which was the 100-1 winner of the Grand National in 1967?
a) Anglo; b) Foinavon; c) Ayala

Fence No 16: The Water, 2ft 6in hedge fence followed by a 12ft 6in spread of water
Points value: Three

Which County won the John Player cricket league in 1986?
a) Sussex; b) Middlesex; c) Hampshire

ANSWERS

JUMP TO IT (Page 87): 1. 4 miles 865 yards; 2. Rocky Marciano; 3. Dick Saunders; 4. Bobby Charlton.

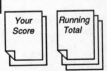

Fence No 17: Thorn fence, 4ft 6in;
dressed with gorse
Points value: Two

With which event do you associate the name Sergei Bubka?
a) Hammer; b) Triple Jump; c) Pole Vault

Fence No 18: Thorn fence, 4ft 7in high;
dressed with gorse
Points value: Two

Which soccer club is nicknamed the Bees?
a) Brentford; b) Bolton; c) Bury

Fence No 19: Open Ditch, ditch 6ft, fence 5ft;
dressed with spruce
Points value: Three

Who won a record 18 tournaments on the US golf circuit in 1945?
a) Sam Snead; b) Ben Hogan; c) Byron Nelson

Fence No 20: Thorn fence, 4ft 10in high;
dressed with fir
Points value: Two

Which country beat England in the 1987 World Cup cricket final?
a) India; b)Australia; c) Pakistan

Fence No 21: Thorn fence, 4ft 10in high;
dressed with fir
Points value: Two

Which footballer did AC Milan buy for £5.5 million in 1987?
a) Diego Maradona; b) Karl-Heinz Rummenigge; c) Ruud Gulllitt

Fence No 22: Becher's Brook, 4ft 10in high
fence followed by 5ft 6in brook
Points value: Seven

Which was the second of Fred Winter's winning National rides?
a) Sundew; b) Kilmore; c) Nicolaus Silver

Your Score

Running Total

ANSWERS

JUMP TO IT (Page 88): 5. Geoff Boycott; 6. Gay Trip; 7. Dundee United;
8. 50-1; 9. Reynoldstown; 10. Northants.

Fence No 23: Thorn fence, 4ft 6in high; dressed with fir
Points value: Two

With which sport do you associate the name of Richard Bergmann, who represented Austria before the war and England in post-war internationals?

a) Hockey; b) Table Tennis; c) Squash

 Fence No 24: Canal Turn, fence 5ft high; dressed with fir
Points value: Five

Who was the first woman rider to complete the Aintree course in the Grand National?

a) Charlotte Brew; b) Geraldine Rees; c) Gee Armytage

 Fence No 25: Valentine's Brook, 5ft thorn fence followed by 5ft 6in brook
Points value: Five

In which round did Barry McGuigan stop Nicky Perez in his comeback fight in London in 1988?

a) fourth; b) fifth; c) sixth

 Fence No 26: Thorn fence, 5ft high; dressed with fir
Points value: Two

Which Wimbledon men's singles champion was a former holder of the world table tennis championship?

a) Yvon Petra; b) Fred Perry; c) Donald Budge

 Fence No 27: Open ditch, 6ft high followed by 5ft high thorn fence dressed with fir
Points value: Three

With which County team was England cricket manager Micky Stewart an established batsman and top-flight slip fielder?

a) Middlesex; b) Essex; c) Surrey

ANSWERS

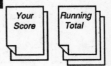

Your Score | Running Total

JUMP TO IT (Page 89): 11. Ice Skating; 12. Ian Botham; 13. Trevor Berbick; 14. Plymouth; 15. Foinavon; 16. Hampshire.

Fence No 28: 5ft thorn fence followed by a ditch 5ft 6in wide
Points value: Three

From which club did Liverpool manager Kenny Dalglish sign Ray Houghton in 1987?
a) Luton Town; b) Oxford United; c) Leicester City

 Fence No 29: Thorn fence 4ft 7in high; dressed with gorse
Points value: Two

Who was the only athlete to win two individual gold medals on the track in the 1978 Commonwealth Games?
a) John Walker; b) Allan Wells; c) Henry Rono

 Fence No 30: Thorn fence, 4ft 6in high; dressed with gorse
Points value: Two

Who in 1976 became the first batsman since Don Bradman to score a century before lunch on the first day of a Test match?
a) Hanif Mohammad; b) Majid Khan; c) Sunil Gavaskar

 **For the final ten points that will take you on the punishing 494 yard run around the 'Elbow' to the finishing post you must name the two horses that were involved in a thrilling finish to the 1973 Grand National. You need to name both horses to get the points. They are both included among the following ten horses:**

Specify, Red Alligator, L'Escargot, Red Rum, Aldaniti, Rubstic, Crisp, Team Spirit, Jay Trump, Rag Trade.

ANSWERS

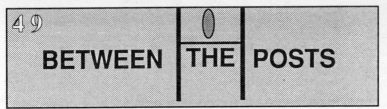

BETWEEN THE POSTS

Award yourself two points for each correct answer to the
following seven Rugby questions.
Average score: 4 Greavsie: 6

1. Which was the only team to beat the All Blacks during their 1978 tour, winning by 12 points to nil?

a) Llanelli; b) Munster; c) Leicester

2. Who captained Wigan in the Rugby League Challenge Cup Final six times between 1958 and 1966?

a) Eric Ashton; b) Alex Murphy; c) David Watkins

3. Which player has scored most points in a test series for the British Lions?

a) JPR Williams; b) Tom Kiernan; c) Andy Irvine

4. Who scored tries in a record 11 successive first division Rugby League matches in 1985?

a) Ellery Hanley; b) David Noble; c) Gary Prohm

5. Which player was capped 44 times by Wales and won an Olympic silver medal as a sprinter?

a) Ken Jones; b) Steve Fenwick; c) Maurice Richards

6. Who scored 18 points for the British Lions against the Springboks in Cape Town in 1980?

a) John Carleton; b) Tony Ward; c) Dusty Hare

7. Which Rugby League club paid £14,000 for free-scoring Newport and Wales centre Keith Jarrett in 1969?

a) Featherstone; b) Hull Kingston Rovers; c) Barrow

ANSWERS

JUMP TO IT (Page 91): 23. Table Tennis; 24. Geraldine Rees; 25. Fourth round; 26. Fred Perry; 27. Surrey.

How closely do you follow the football transfer market? Here are 30 of the major deals since 1960. In each deal we have missed out either the selling or buying club. Award yourself two points for each blank that you can fill. Average score: 38 Greavsie: 44

FEE	PLAYER	FROM	TO	YEAR
£116,000	Denis Law		Man. United	1962
£80,000	Fred Pickering	Blackburn		1964
£100,000	Tony Hateley		Liverpool	1967
£96,000	Mike England	Blackburn		1966
£90,000	Bobby Gould		Arsenal	1968
£100,000	Jim Baxter	Sunderland		1967
£72,000	Charlie Cooke		Chelsea	1966
£125,000	Martin Chivers	S'thampton		1961
£110,000	Alan Ball		Everton	1966
£165,000	Allan Clarke	Leicester		1969
£200,000	Rodney Marsh		Man. City	1972
£200,000	Bruce Rioch	Aston Villa		1974
£200,000	Lou Macari		Man. United	1973
£240,000	Alan Hudson	Chelsea		1974

ANSWERS

JUMP TO IT (Page 92): 28. Oxford United; 29. Henry Rono (5,000 metres and steeplechase); 30. Majid Khan. Finish: Red Rum and Crisp.

THE TRANSFER TRAIL

FEE	PLAYER	FROM	TO	YEAR
£250,000	Asa Hartford		Man. City	1974
£300,000	Martin Dobson	Burnley		1974
£340,000	Peter Shilton		Stoke	1974
£375,000	Ricky Villa	Racing Club		1978
£400,000	John Deehan		West Brom	1979
£425,000	Andy King	Everton		1980
£430,000	Ray Stewart		West Ham	1979
£450,000	Alan Brazil	Ipswich		1983
£465,000	Gerry Francis		C. Palace	1979
£500,000	Lee Chapman	Stoke		1982
£500,000	Remi Moses		Man. United	1981
£500,000	Frank Gray	Leeds		1979
£590,000	Chris Waddle		Tottenham	1985
£600,000	John Gidman	Aston Villa		1979
£700,000	Paul Walsh		Liverpool	1984
£900,000	Trevor Francis	Man. City		1982

ANSWERS

BETWEEN THE POSTS (Page 93): 1. Munster; 2. Eric Ashton; 3. Tom Kieman; 4. Gary Prohm; 5. Ken Jones; 6. Tony Ward; 7. Barrow.

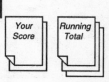

51

ROUNDERS

The sports puzzle that will have you going in circles

Each clue leads to a familiar sports word or name. The LAST letter of each word or name is the FIRST letter of the next. Two points for each correct answer and a 5-point bonus if you complete the circle.
Average score: 8
Greavsie: 17

1	Surname of the Great White Shark of the fairways (6).
2	David, Leicester City's FA Cup Final captain in 1969 (4)
3	This is where you will find Boothferry Park (4).
4	Not the tight-head front-row forward (5).
5	Duncan, the tragic hero of Old Trafford (7).
6	The link between Benaud, Lock, Bedi and Cook (4).

 Your Score

 Running Total

ANSWERS

THE TRANSFER TRAIL (Page 94)): Law (Torino); Pickering (Everton); Hateley (Chelsea); England (Spurs); Gould (Coventry); Baxter (Nottm. Forest); Cooke (Dundee); Chivers (Spurs); Ball (Blackpool); Clarke (Leeds); Marsh (QPR); Rioch (Derby); Macari (Celtic); Hudson (Stoke).

52

UP FOR T'CUP

We have selected four years from post-war FA Cup competitions and present a question on each round, starting—as with First Division teams—at the third. The later the round the tougher the question, and the higher the points value.

Average score: 48 Greavsie: 54

THE YEAR: 1957

Third round. Points value: 1
Cup holders Manchester City lose 5-4 in a replay to which club that had beaten them at Wembley in 1955?

Fourth round. Points value: 2
Bournemouth become the 1957 giantkillers. In this round they beat which club managed by Stan Cullis?

Fifth round. Points value: 3
Bournemouth strike again. They knock out which team that has England international Ted Ditchburn in goal?

Sixth round. Points value: 4
Arsenal, London's sole survivors, go out after a replay against which club from The Hawthorns?

Semi-final. Points value: 5
Manchester United reach the Final by knocking out which Midlands club that were runners-up in 1956?

Final. Points value: 6
Aston Villa beat Manchester United 2-1 after which goalkeeper had fractured his cheekbone in a collision?

ANSWERS

THE TRANSFER TRAIL (Page 95)): Hartford (West Brom); Dobson (Everton); Shilton (Leicester); Villa (Spurs); Deehan (Aston Villa); King (QPR); Stewart (Dundee United); Brazil (Spurs); Gerry Francis (QPR); Chapman (Arsenal); Moses (West Brom); Gray (Nottm Forest); Waddle (Newcastle); Gidman (Everton); Walsh (Luton); Trevor Francis (Sampdoria).

Your Score

Running Total

UP FOR T'CUP

THE YEAR: 1967

Third round. Points value: 1
West Ham, winners in 1964, are knocked out by which team that includes winger Don Rogers?

Fourth round. Points value: 2
Norwich City knock out which team who go on to win the League championship?

Fifth round. Points value: 3
Leeds United go to two replays before beating which club who get their revenge at Wembley six years later?

Sixth round. Points value: 4
Ian Storey-Moore completes a hat-trick in the last minute for Forest to beat which Cup-holding team?

Semi-final. Points value: 5
Which Chelsea centre-forward heads the goal that beats Leeds to set up an all-London Final?

Final. Points value: 6
Which Scottish international winger scores the first goal for Spurs to put them on the way to a 2-1 victory?

UP FOR T'CUP

THE YEAR: 1977

 Third round. Points value: 1
Northwich Victoria are the shock side, beating which team that reaches Wembley 7 years later?

 Fourth round. Points value: 2
Which team from Boundary Park ends the Northwich Victoria giantkilling run with a 3-1 victory?

 Fifth round. Points value: 3
Which North-East team—that has never won the FA Cup—hammer Arsenal 4-1?

 Sixth round. Points value: 4
Which Scottish international left winger scores the goal that gives Leeds a 1-0 victory at Wolves?

 Semi-final. Points value: 5
Against which team do Liverpool win 3-0 in a semi-final replay at Maine Road?

 Final. Points value: 6
Who is credited with Manchester United's second goal in their 2-1 win over Liverpool at Wembley?

ANSWERS

UP FOR TCUP—1957 (Page 97): Third round: Newcastle United; Fourth round: Wolves; Fifth round: Spurs; Sixth round: West Bromwich Albion; Semi-final: Birmingham City; Final: Ray Wood.

Your Score | Running Total

UP FOR T'CUP

THE YEAR: 1987

Third round. Points value: 1
Which team beats holders Liverpool 3-0 in a third round second replay?

Fourth round. Points value: 2
Which Third Division club from Springfield Park beats First Division Norwich City 1-0?

Fifth round. Points value: 3
Who scores his 35th goal of the season from the penalty spot to give Spurs a 1-0 win over Newcastle?

Sixth round. Points value: 4
Who nets two late goals against Sheffield Wednesday to put Coventry into their first ever FA Cup semi-final?

Semi-final. Points value: 5
Which team is beaten 3-2 in extra-time by Coventry with a goal by Dave Bennett?

Final. Points value: 6
Which Tottenham player deflects the ball into this own net to give Coventry a shock FA Cup Final victory?

Your Score   Running Total

ANSWERS

UP FOR T'CUP—1967 (Page 98): Third round: Swindon Town; Fourth round: Manchester United; Fifth round: Sunderland; Sixth round: Everton; Semi-final: Tony Hateley; Final: Jimmy Robertson.

100

53 IAN BOTHAM

*Award yourself one point for each
question you can answer about
cricketer Ian Botham*
Average score: 5 Greavsie: 6

1. In which County was he born in 1955?

2. Who was Somerset captain when Ian made his County debut?

3. Against which country did he make his England Test debut in 1977?

4. On which ground in 1978 did he become the first cricketer to take eight wickets and score a century in the same Test?

5. Against which County did he score a career best 228 for Somerset in 1980?

6. Which Indian batsman did he dismiss for his 100th Test victim in record time at Lord's in 1979?

7. In how many Tests did he complete the 100 wickets, 1,000 runs double — another record?

8. For which Football League first-team did he play?

9. On which ground did he score his 'miraculous' match-turning 149 not out against Australia in 1981?

10. What is the name of the chairman who signed him for Worcestershire following his bust-up with Somerset?

ANSWERS

UP FOR TCUP—1977 (Page 99): Third round: Watford; Fourth round: Oldham Athletic; Fifth round: Middlesbrough; Sixth round: Eddie Gray; Semi-final: Everton; Final: Jimmy Greenhoff.

Your Score

Running Total

54 HARK WHO'S TALKING

There are quotes on this page from six famous sports personalities. Score two points for each that you correctly identify.
Average score: 6 Greavsie: 10

1. "A lot of people thought I was just a slippery Cockney boy with a few jokes. It has taken one of the biggest clubs in the world to acknowledge what I can do."
a) John Bond; b) Terry Venables; c) Dave Bassett

2. "I think Gabriela and I will become the new Martina and Chris. We can be at the top for a long time to come."
a) Steffi Graf; b) Hana Mandlikova; c) Andrea Jaeger

3. "Reference Point kept looking at the crowd in the home straight as if he was happy to be alive."
a) Pat Eddery; b) Walter Swinburn; c) Steve Cauthen

4. "People criticised me for not making a better show. But they just didn't understand what had happened. He had destroyed my motivation with that one effort. It was the first of the competition and it was all over. It just blew my mind."
a) Allan Wells; b) Lynn Davies; c) Daley Thompson

5. "If we'd caught him just seconds earlier that would have been it. The bell wouldn't have saved him. We didn't do badly for an old bum and a cripple, did we?"
a) Larry Holmes; b) John Conteh; c) Henry Cooper

6. "We should give Steve Davis some sort of a handicap, like take his cue away!"
a) Terry Griffiths; b) Dennis Taylor; c) Eddie Charlton

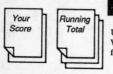

Your Score

Running Total

ANSWERS

UP FOR T'CUP—1987 (Page 100): Third round: Luton Town; Fourth round: Wigan Athletic; Fifth round: Clive Allen; Sixth round: Keith Houchen; Semi-final: Leeds United; Final: Gary Mabbutt.

55 SPORTS SLEUTH

Here are four sporting mysteries for you to solve. Award yourself four points for each correct answer.
Average score: 8 Greavsie: 12

1. Nat Lofthouse became a national hero as the 'Lion of Vienna' after racing 50 yards to score a wonder goal that lifted England to a dramatic 3-2 victory over Austria in 1952. The mystery is: **Why didn't Lofthouse know he had scored the winning goal?** *Clue: Count to ten!*

2. Miruts 'The Shifter' Yifter, double Olympic gold medallist in the 1980 Games, was one of the favourites for a medal in the 5,000 metres final in the 1972 Games in Munich. When the starter called the runners to their marks Yifter was missing. The mystery is: **Why did Yifter miss the race?** *Clue: He <u>had</u> to run!*

3. All the players who took part in the 1970 World Cup in Mexico were awarded a commemorative medal. The mystery is: **Why was Alan Ball the only England player who arrived home without a medal?** *Clue: It should not throw you for long!*

4. Muhammad Ali was famous for his verbal outbursts at title fight weigh-ins. But he was speechless when weighing in for his defence against Britain's Richard Dunn in Munich in 1976. The mystery is: **What silenced the Louisville Lip?** *Clue: He went down, but without a count.*

ANSWERS

HOW WELL D'YOU KNOW IAN BOTHAM? (Page 101): 1. Cheshire; 2. Brian Close; 3. Australia; 4. Lord's (v Pakistan); 5. Gloucestershire; 6. Sunil Gavaskar; 7. 21 Tests; 8. Scunthorpe; 9. Headingley; 10. Duncan Fearnley.

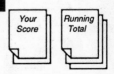

Your Score   *Running Total*

56 GUESS THE GUEST

*See how quickly you can identify
a star sportsman from the clues.*
Average score: 4 Greavsie: 6

For 12 points: Our mystery guest was born in Harrow on April 28, 1942, and started his sporting career after studying at Cambridge University.

For 10 points: While at Cambridge between 1961 and 1964 he amassed what remains a university record haul of 4,348 runs in first-class cricket.

For 8 points: A wicket-keeper in his early days, he developed into a highly regarded slip fielder and he was a specialist batsman.

For 6 points: In 1971 he became captain of Middlesex, and in 39 Tests for England he scored 1442 runs.

For 4 points: He was noted for his leadership qualities and tactical awareness, and was chosen to succeed Tony Greig as England captain.

For 2 points: In 1981 he took over from Ian Botham in a comeback as England captain, and he led the team that retained the Ashes with Botham-inspired victories over the Australians.

Your Score	Running Total

ANSWERS

HARK WHO'S TALKING (Page 102): 1. Terry Venables (while in charge at Barcelona); 2. Steffi Graf; 3. Steve Cauthen (after winning the 1987 Derby); 4. Lynn Davies (after Bob Beamon's winning 29ft long jump in the 1968 Olympics); 5. Henry Cooper (after knocking down Cassius Clay in their first fight); 6. Terry Griffiths.

57 ON YER BIKE!

There are eight questions here all related to sport on two wheels. Award yourself two points for each correct answer.

Average score: 4
Greavsie: 6

 1. Was it Reg Harris, Alan Bannister or Norman Sheil who won two silver medals on the track in the 1948 Olympics?

2. Was Bill Ivy, Geoff Duke or Freddie Spencer first to win the 250cc and 500cc world titles in the same year?

 3. Was Brian Robinson or Tommy Simpson the first Englishman to wear the yellow jersey in the Tour de France?

4. Did Barry Briggs, Ivan Mauger or Ove Fundin score a record 201 points in world championship speedway?

 5. Was Jacques Anquetil, Bernard Hinault or Eddy Merckx first to win the Tour de France five times?

6. Did Mike Hailwood win his first senior TT 500cc race in 1961 on a Honda, an MV Augusta or a Norton?

 7. Was it Ian Hallam, Tony Doyle or Ian Steele who won Britain's only world title in Barcelona in 1984?

8. Was David Jessup, Malcolm Simmons or Michael Lee the first Briton to win the world long track speedway title?

ANSWERS

SPORTS SLEUTH (Page 103): 1. Lofthouse was knocked unconscious in a collision with the goalkeeper; 2. Yifter answered an urgent call of nature and was in the toilet, unaware that the race had started; 3. Ball was so disgusted with England's quarter-final defeat by West Germany that he threw his medal out of a Mexican hotel window; 4. As Ali and his entourage stepped on to the stage for the weigh-in it collapsed. The weigh-in was delayed for an hour.

 Your Score

 Running Total

58

TAKE

CARD

Take a card — any card — on each of the following 12 pages and see if you can deal yourself a winning hand. Read each of the four questions on the page and then decide which one of them you feel confident you can answer. You must be all-correct with your answer to get the points value of the card. Remember, you can score only off one card on each page.

Average score: 36
Greavsie: 38

For 2 points:

Name the two rival captains in the FA Cup Final between Liverpool and Wimbledon at Wembley in 1988

For 3 points:

Name three of the four British athletes who won gold medals in the men's events at the 1980 Olympics in Moscow

For 4 points:

Name four of the six grounds used during the 1981 Test series in which England beat the Aussie team led by Kim Hughes

For 5 points:

Name five of the six boxers that Henry Cooper fought in European heavyweight title fights

ANSWERS

ON YER BIKE (Page 105): 1. Reg Harris; 2. Freddie Spencer (1985); 3. Tommy Simpson (1962); 4. Barry Briggs; 5. Jacques Anquetil; 6. Norton; 7. Tony Doyle; 8. Michael Lee.

Your Score

Running Total

For 2 points:

Name the
first two
Welsh Rugby
players to
win more
than 50
international
caps

For 3 points:

Name the
first three
British
drivers to
win the
world
motor racing
championship

For 4 points:

Name four of the
eight English
classic winners
ridden by former
champion jockey
Joe Mercer
between
1953 and 1981

For 5 points:

Name five
of the six
British golfers
who have
captured
the Open
championship
since the war

Your Score

Running Total

ANSWERS

The Take A Card answers for this hand are on page 110.

For 2 points:

Name the two players who won the women's doubles title at Wimbledon five times between 1967 and 1973

For 3 points:

Name the three West Ham players who were in England's World Cup winning team in 1966

For 4 points:

Name four of the opponents Mike Tyson met in his first five contests with a world title at stake

For 5 points:

Name five of the nine riders who have won the flat racing jockeys' championship since 1940.

ANSWERS

TAKE A CARD (Page 107): 2: Alan Hansen and Dave Beasant; 3: Allan Wells, Steve Ovett, Sebastian Coe, Daley Thompson; 4. Trent Bridge, Lord's, Headingley, Edgbaston, Old Trafford, The Oval; 5. Ingemar Johansson, Brian London, Karl Mildenberger, Piero Tomasoni, Jose Urtain, Joe Bugner.

For 2 points:

Name the two
horses that
finished first
and second
in the
1988 Grand
National
at Aintree

For 3 points:

Name three
of the four
clubs that
Tommy Docherty
played for
before
becoming
a manager

For 4 points:

Name four of
the six opponents
Steve Davis
has played in
world snooker
championship
finals between
1981 and 1988

For 5 points:

Name five of
the seven players
who were
in Liverpool's
first two
European Cup
winning teams
in 1977 and 1978

Your Score

Running Total

ANSWERS

TAKE A CARD (Page 108): 2: JPR Williams and Gareth Edwards; 3. Mike
Hawthorn, Graham Hill, Jim Clark; 4. Ambiguity, Provoke, Bustino, Light
Cavalary, Cut Above, Brigadier Gerard, Highclere, One in a Million; 5. Fred
Daly, Henry Cotton, Max Faulkner, Tony Jacklin, Sandy Lyle, Nick Faldo.

For 2 points:

Name the two clubs other than Celtic and Rangers who have won the Scottish Premier Division championship

For 3 points:

Name the three Australian golfers who have won the British Open championship since the war

For 4 points:

Name four of the five post-war English batsmen who have scored 1,000 runs in a season more than 20 times

For 5 points:

Name each of the five Football League clubs that have won the FA Cup more than five times

ANSWERS

TAKE A CARD (Page 109): 2: Billie-Jean King and Rosie Casals; 3: Bobby Moore, Geoff Hurst, Martin Peters; 4. Trevor Berbick, James Smith, Pinklon Thomas, Tony Tucker, Tyrell Biggs; 5. Gordon Richards, Harry Wragg, Doug Smith, Scobie Breasley, Lester Piggott, Willie Carson, Pat Eddery, Joe Mercer, Steve Cauthen.

For 2 points:

Name the two
clubs that
Nottingham Forest
defeated in
their European
Cup Finals
of 1979
and 1980

For 3 points:

Name the only
three boxers to
beat former
world heavyweight
champion
Joe Louis
in his 66 fight
ring career

For 4 points:

Name the four
events in which
Carl Lewis
won gold
medals in
the 1984
Olympic Games
in Los Angeles

For 5 points:

Name five of
the eight
British boxers
who have
held the
world flyweight
championship
since 1930

Your
Score

Running
Total

ANSWERS

TAKE A CARD (Page 110): 2: Rhyme 'n' Reason and Durham Edition; 3: Celtic, Preston, Arsenal, Chelsea; 4: Doug Mountjoy, Cliff Thorburn, Jimmy White, Dennis Taylor, Joe Johnson, Terry Griffiths; 5: Ray Clemence, Phil Neal, Ray Kennedy, Emlyn Hughes, Jimmy Case, Steve Heighway, Terry McDermott.

For 2 points:

Name the two golfers who contested a play-off for the British Open title at St Andrews in 1970

For 3 points:

Name the first three England footballers to win more than 100 international caps

For 4 points:

Name four of the five boxers who beat Muhammad Ali during his 61-fight professional ring career

For 5 points:

Name each of the five English flat racing classics in the order that they are run every year

ANSWERS

TAKE A CARD Page 111): 2: Aberdeen and Dundee United; 3: Peter Thomson, Kel Nagle, Greg Norman; 4: Colin Cowdrey, Geoff Boycott, Dennis Amiss, Tom Graveney, John Edrich; 5. Aston Villa, Tottenham, Blackburn Rovers, Manchester United, Newcastle United.

2

For 2 points:

Name the two teams that contested the 1988 Rugby League Challenge Cup Final at Wembley

3

For 3 points:

Name three of the four clubs with which Scottish international Denis Law played during his career

4

For 4 points:

Name the four events in which Dutch housewife Fanny Blankers-Koen won gold medals in the 1948 Olympics

5

For 5 points:

Name five of the eight horses on which Lester Piggott finished first in the St Leger

Your Score

Running Total

ANSWERS

TAKE A CARD (Page 112): 2: Malmo and Hamburg; 3: Max Schmeling, Ezzard Charles, Rocky Marciano; 4: 100 metres, 200 metres, long jump, 4 x 100 metres relay; 5: Jackie Brown, Benny Lynch, Peter Kane, Jackie Paterson, Rinty Monaghan, Terry Allen, Walter McGowan, Charlie Magri.

For 2 points:

Name the two
Counties with
which former
England cricket
captain
Bob Willis
played during
his career

For 3 points:

Name three
of the four
runners-up
in these football
World Cup
tournaments:
1938, 1950
1974, 1982

For 4 points:

Name the four
weights at
which history
making boxer
Tommy
Hearns
has been
world champion

For 5 points:

Name five of
the six players
who have
been elected
European
Footballer
of the Year
more than once

ANSWERS

TAKE A CARD (Page 113): 2: Jack Nicklaus and Doug Sanders; 3: Billy Wright, Bobby Charlton and Bobby Moore; 4: Joe Frazier, Ken Norton, Leon Spinks, Larry Holmes, Trevor Berbick; 5: 1,000 Guineas, 2,000 Guineas, Derby, Oaks, St. Leger.

For 2 points:

Name the two Rugby-playing brothers who were half back partners for France and known as the 'Two Fleas'

For 3 points:

Name the three British boxers who have held the world welterweight title since the First World War

For 4 points:

Name four of the five wicket-keepers who have made more than 190 dismissals in Test cricket

For 5 points:

Name five of the eight men who have managed Manchester United in post-war football

Your Score

Running Total

ANSWERS

TAKE A CARD (Page 114): 2: Wigan and Halifax; 3: Huddersfield Town, Manchester City, Torino, Manchester United; 4: 100 metres, 200 metres, 80 metres hurdles, 4 x 100 metres relay; 5: St Paddy, Aurelius, Ribocco, Ribero, Nijinsky, Athens Wood, Boucher, Commanche Run.

For 2 points:

Name the team against which Graeme Hick scored 405 not out in 1988 and also the ground on which he achieved the feat

For 3 points:

Name the three events in which Emil Zatopek won three gold medals in the 1952 Olympics in Helsinki

For 4 points:

Name the four opponents that Australian Rod Laver beat in the four Wimbledon singles finals that he won

For 5 points:

Name the five British football clubs for which Trevor Francis has played during his career

ANSWERS

TAKE A CARD (Page 115): 2: Surrey and Warwickshire; 3: Hungary, Brazil, Holland, West Germany; 4: Welterweight, light-middle, middle and light-heavyweight; 5: Alfredo di Stefano, Johan Cruyff, Franz Beckenbauer, Kevin Keegan, Karl-Heinz Rummenigge, Michel Platini.

For 2 points:

Name the two football teams that met in the first European Cup Final that was staged in Paris in 1956

For 3 points:

Name three of the four British women athletes who have won gold medals in Olympic competition

For 4 points:

Name the four British boxers who challenged Muhammad Ali in world heavyweight championship contests

For 5 points:

Name five of the six League clubs other than Liverpool who have won the First Division championship since 1970

ANSWERS

Your Score   Running Total

TAKE A CARD (Page 116): 2: Guy and Lilian Camberabero; 3: Ted (Kid) Lewis, John H. Stracey, Lloyd Honeyghan; 4: Rodney Marsh, Alan Knott, Wasim Bari, Godfrey Evans, Syed Kirmani; 5: Matt Busby, Wilf McGuinness, Frank O'Farrell, Tommy Docherty, Dave Sexton, Ron Atkinson, Alex Ferguson.

118

59 SEARCH FOR A CLUB

How many Football League and Scottish League clubs can you find in this grid? There are 18 names. Some appear in straightforward, left-to-right formations, others are printed in reverse or diagonally across the page. Award yourself one point for each club that you find.

Average score: 11 Greavsie: 14

```
N W O T H C I W S P I
A B E R D E E N Z A N
I A R S E N A L S L R
N Y P E T A Y R R L U
R W R E X H A M E I B
E B I Q L E A V G V K
B U P G B K T M N N C
I R S W A N S E A O A
H Y E E D N U D R T L
E L T S A C W E N S B
S R E V O R H T I A R
```

ANSWERS

TAKE A CARD (Page 117): 2: Somerset, at Taunton; 3: 5,000 metres, 10,000 metres and the marathon; 4: Chuck McKinley, Martin Mulligan, Tony Roche, John Newcombe; 5: Birmingham City, Nottingham Forest, Manchester City, Glasgow Rangers, Queen's Park Rangers.

60 THE NAME GAME

EACH clue leads to a well-known name. Put the initials in the appropriate squares to identify a champion sportsman. Two points for each correct answer, plus a bonus of ten points for completing the main name.

Average score: 18 Greavsie: 20

1	2	3	4	5				
6	7	8	9	10	11	12	13	14

11 & 4	Did this batsman from Victoria skipper Australia at the gallop?
8 & 2	He won the first of his world motor racing championships in a Ferrari in 1975.
14 & 3	He switched from breakfast television to present suppertime sport on ITV.
13 & 10	This skilful Scot wore the No. 9 shirt in Everton's 1966 FA Cup-winning team.
5 & 7	He won a silver medal for Britain in the javelin event in the 1984 LA Olympics.
1 & 12	This boxer first became world champion by outpointing Ken Norton in 1978.
9 & 6	Without question, he was the first player to hold the European Cup in 1977.

ANSWERS

TAKE A CARD (Page 118): 2: Real Madrid, Stade de Rheims; 3: Mary Rand, Ann Packer, Mary Peters, Tessa Sanderson; 4: Henry Cooper, Brian London, Joe Bugner, Richard Dunn; 5: Arsenal, Derby County, Leeds United, Nottingham Forest, Aston Villa, Everton.

120

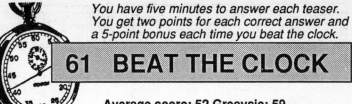

You have five minutes to answer each teaser.
You get two points for each correct answer and
a 5-point bonus each time you beat the clock.

61 BEAT THE CLOCK

Average score: 52 Greavsie: 59

1. Name the eight football clubs that have won the European Cup more than once.

2. Name the five Derby winners trained by Vincent O'Brien.

3. Name the 11 England cricketers who played against Australia in the 1987 World Cup Final.

4. Name the nine men who have won the Blue Riband of the track— the 1,500 metres—in post-war Olympiads.

5. Name the six men who have managed the England football team, including in a caretaker capacity.

ANSWERS

Your Score

Running Total

Can you fill in the blanks in the following sporting headlines? Award yourself one point for each gap that you fill.

Average score: 7
Greavsie: 9

1.
BLANK STOPS ROCKY MATTIOLI IN 8TH TO WIN WORLD TITLE

2.
BLANK FINISHES 1 AND 2 IN 1988 BADMINTON TRIALS

3.
WIMBLEDON REACH WEMBLEY WITH SEMI-FINAL WIN OVER BLANK

4.
BLANK BECOMES OLDEST WINNER OF THE BRITISH OPEN GOLF TITLE

5.
BLANK PIPS McKENLEY IN 400 METRES FINAL AT WEMBLEY

6.
BLANK BECOMES THE FIRST PLAYER SENT OFF IN AN FA CUP FINAL

7.
GATTING SUCCEEDS BLANK AS ENGLAND SKIPPER

8.
FULL BACK BLANK SCORES HIS 3,000TH POINT FOR LEICESTER

9.
BLANK FALLS IN OLYMPIC FINAL COLLISION WITH ZOLA BUDD

10.
BLANK TAKES ONE WICKET AS LAKER SETS NEW RECORD WITH 19 FOR 90

11.
BLANK TRIUMPHS ON HENBIT FOR HIS SECOND SUCCESSIVE DERBY VICTORY

14.
BLANK NETS HIS 349TH GOAL FOR EVERTON

12.
BLANK IS FIRST TO CONQUER HOLMES

13.
BLANK FOLLOWS TAYLOR AS WATFORD MANAGER

ANSWERS

Your Score

Running Total

Simply answer true or false to the following statements.
Two points for each correct answer.
Average score: 6 Greavsie: 8

63 TRUE OR FALSE?

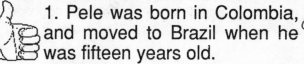
1. Pele was born in Colombia, and moved to Brazil when he was fifteen years old.

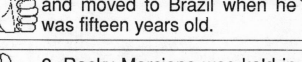
2. Rocky Marciano was ko'd in the 1948 Olympic semi-finals by eventual winner Rafael Iglesis

3. Denis Compton played his last competitive football match for Arsenal in the 1950 Cup Final.

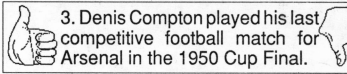
4. Gordon Banks used to bag coal for a living before becoming a professional footballer.

5. Ian Botham was invited to join Crystal Palace before he made his name in cricket.

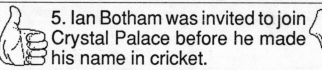

ANSWERS

BEAT THE CLOCK (Page 121): 1. Real Madrid, Benfica, AC Milan, Inter-Milan, Ajax, Bayern Munich, Liverpool, Nottingham Forest; 2. Larkspur, Sir Ivor, Nijinksy, Roberto, The Minstrel. 3. Graham Gooch, Tim Robinson, Bill Athey, Mike Gatting, Allan Lamb, Paul Downton, John Emburey, Phil DeFreitas, Neil Foster, Gladstone Small, Eddie Hemmings. 4. Henry Eriksson (1948), Josef Barthel (1952), Ronnie Delany (1956), Herb Elliott (1960), Peter Snell (1964), Kip Keino (1968), Pekka Vassala (1972), John Walker (1976), Seb Coe (1980 and 1984). 5. Walter Winterbottom, Alf Ramsey, Joe Mercer, Don Revie, Ron Greenwood, Bobby Robson.

Your
Score

Running
Total

123

64

ROUNDERS

*The sports puzzle
that will have you
going in circles*

Each clue leads to a familiar sports word
or surname. The LAST letter of each word
or name is the FIRST letter of the next.
Two points for each correct answer
and a 5-point bonus if you
complete the circle.
**Average score: 11
Greavsie: 13**

1	The Park where Cardiff City are at home (6).
2	John Bond and Ken Brown have managed this club (7).
3	It always leads at the greyhound track (4).
4	An Essex wicket-keeper will give you direction (4).
5	The Derby defender who succeeded Bobby Moore (4).
6	Roberto, who won and lost to Sugar Ray Leonard (5).

Your Score

Running Total

ANSWERS

HEADLINE MAKERS (Page 122): 1. Maurice Hope; 2. Ian Stark; 3. Luton Town; 4. Roberto de Vicenzo; 4. Arthur Wint; 6. Kevin Moran; 7. David Gower; 8. Dusty Hare; 9. Mary Decker; 10. Tony Lock; 11. Willie Carson; 12. Michael Spinks; 13. Dave Bassett; 14. Dixie Dean.

DIEGO MARADONA

Award yourself one point for each question you can answer about footballer Diego Maradona
Average score: 6 Greavsie: 8

1. In which year was he born?

2. With which Argentinian club was he playing before his move to Europe?

3. Did he play for Argentina in the 1978 World Cup Final—yes or no?

4. Which Spanish club bought him for £5million in 1982?

5. Against which country was he sent off during the 1982 World Cup finals in Spain?

6. Within £500,000—what was the world record transfer fee when he switched to Italian football in 1984?

7. Which Italian League club did he join?

8. From which World Cup skipper did he take over as captain of the Argentinian team?

9. Against which country did he score two goals in the 1986 World Cup semi-final?

10. With which hand did he put the ball into the net past Peter Shilton for the first Argentinian goal in the 1986 World Cup match against England?

ANSWERS

TRUE OR FALSE? (Page 123): 1. False (Pele was born in Brazil); 2. False (Rocky Marciano was never an Olympic boxer); 3. False (Denis played a final League match against Portsmouth four days later and scored two goals); 4. True (Gordon was a coalbagger in Sheffield before joining Chesterfield); 5. True (Bert Head, then Crystal Palace manager, approached Botham's parents when Ian was 15).

Your Score

Running Total

How closely do you watch sport on television? This quiz will test your knowledge of who's who on TV sport. Two points for each correct answer.
Average score: 16 Greavsie: 20

66: SPORT ON THE BOX

1. Who was the BBCtv commentator for the 1966 World Cup Final?
a) Raymond Glendenning
b) Peter Dimmock
c) Kenneth Wolstenholme

2. Who was the original presenter of ITV's On the Ball?
a) Hugh Johns
b) Ian St John
c) Brian Moore

3. Who commentated on the Bruno-Bugner fight in 1987?
a) Reg Gutteridge
b) Harry Carpenter
c) Desmond Lynam

4. Who was a Northern Counties mile champion in his youth?
a) Ron Pickering
b) Alan Parry
c) David Coleman

5. Who is renowned as the BBC's Voice of Racing?
a) Julian Wilson
b) Peter O'Sullevan
c) Jimmy Lindley

6. Who is the regular presenter of ITV's racing on Channel 4?
a) Derek Thompson
b) John Oaksey
c) Brough Scott

Your Score

Running Total

ANSWERS

ROUNDERS (Page 124): 1. Ninian Park; 2. Norwich; 3. Hare; 4. East; 5. Todd; 6. Duran

126

7. Who was the original questionmaster on A Question of Sport?
a) David Vine
b) Barry Davies
c) Alan Weeks

8. Who was Henry Cooper's rival captain in A Question of Sport?
a) Gareth Edwards
b) Cliff Morgan
c) Willie Carson

9. Who took over from Harry Carpenter as presenter of Sportsnight?
a) Jim Rosenthal
b) Elton Welsby
c) Steve Rider

10. Who first presented ITV's World of Sport Saturday show?
a) Eamonn Andrews
b) Dickie Davies
c) Fred Dineage

11. Who commentates on motor racing alongside James Hunt?
a) Dave Lanning
b) Murray Walker
c) Ron Pickering

12. Who regularly introduces BBC's Pro Celebrity Golf?
a) Clive Clark
b) Tony Jacklin
c) Peter Alliss

13. Who is the snooker commentator nicknamed Whispering?
a) Ted Lowe
b) Clive Everton
c) John Pulman

14. Who is the commentator who scored 100 in 78 minutes in 1955?
a) Tom Graveney
b) Ted Dexter
c) Richie Benaud

ANSWERS

Your Score

Running Total

S N O O K E R

BREAK

There are a possible 147 points to be scored on the following seven pages. Each question has been given a points value according to its degree of difficulty. This is a test for all-rounders, not just snooker buffs. Only the 7-point questions are on snooker. This is your cue to start...

Average score: 84 Greavsie: 92

Which Belgian team beat Ajax 1-0 in the 1988 European Cup Winners' Cup Final in Strasbourg?

Was the 'Sultan of Snooker' Joe Davis world champion for a span of 15, 20 or 25 years?

In which Australian city were the 1956 Olympics staged: Sydney, Adelaide or Melbourne?

Which one of these players is a left hander: Eddie Charlton, Joe Johnson, Dean Reynolds, John Spencer, Neal Foulds?

Did British speed ace John Surtees win the world motor drivers' championship once, twice or three times?

ANSWERS

SPORT ON THE BOX (Page 127): 7. David Vine; 8. Cliff Morgan; 9. Steve Rider; 10. Eamonn Andrews; 11. Murray Walker; 12. Peter Alliss; 13. Ted Lowe; 14. Richie Benaud.

Your Score   Running Total

7

Did Steve Davis beat Dennis Taylor or Cliff Thorburn in the semi-finals of the 1988 world championship?

1

Against which light-heavyweight champion did Mark Kaylor have his final fight at Wembley in 1988?

7

Was it Ray Reardon or Graham Miles who won the first BBCtv Pot Black tournament in 1969?

1

Which Scottish international captained Liverpool when they won the FA Cup for the first time in 1965?

7

Did Terry Griffiths beat Stephen Hendry or Jimmy White in the semi-finals of the 1988 world championship?

Your Score

Running Total

ANSWERS

The answers to these Snooker Break questions are on page 132.

130

Was Willie Ormond or Ally MacLeod Scotland manager when they played in the 1974 World Cup finals in Germany?

Who won the £9,000 prize for the highest break of 140 in the 1988 world championships at the Crucible?

Was Roger Bannister's final title-winning race in the 1954 Commonwealth or European championships?

Which one of these players has been world snooker champion: John Spencer, Rex Williams, Eddie Charlton, Jimmy White, Tony Knowles, Willie Thorne?

Against which club did Danny Blanchflower score a penalty in an FA Cup Final at Wembley?

ANSWERS

SNOOKER BREAK (Page 129): 1: Mechelen; 7: 20 years; 1: Melbourne; 7: Dean Reynolds is a left-hander; 1: Surtees won the title once, in 1964.

Which player beat Alex 'Hurricane' Higgins in the 1980 world championship final?

Was Len Hutton or Brian Close the first modern professional captain of the England cricket team?

Did Fred Davis play Walter Donaldson or Horace Lindrum in eight successive world championship finals?

Which jockey won the 1978 St Leger on Julio Mariner—Greville Starkey or Eddie Hide?

Who beat defending champion Steve Davis 10-1 in the first round of the 1982 world championship finals?

ANSWERS

SNOOKER BREAK (Page 130): 7: Cliff Thorburn; 1. Tom Collins; 7: Ray Reardon; 1: Ron Yeats; 7: Jimmy White.

1

Did John Rutherford or Colin Deans captain Scotland in the 1987 Rugby Union World Cup finals?

7

Was it 1980, 1981 or 1982 when Alex Higgins won the world snooker championship at the Crucible?

1

Which British athlete won a silver medal in the women's 3,000 metres in the 1984 Olympics, beating Zola Budd?

7

Was John Parrott or Stephen Hendry beaten 13-11 by Steve Davis in the 1988 Mercantile Credit Snooker Classic final?

1

Which British boxer challenged both Floyd Patterson and Muhammad Ali for the world heavyweight title?

ANSWERS

SNOOKER BREAK (Page 131): 1: Willie Ormond; 7: Steve James; 1: European championships; 7: John Spencer; 1: Burnley, 1962.

Your Score

Running Total

Which player won the women's world snooker championship in 1986—Vera Selby or Alison Fisher?

Who clinched the world motor racing drivers' championship when finishing third in the 1976 Japanese Grand Prix?

Who—at 18—became the youngest winner of a professional snooker title in the 1987 Rothman's Grand Prix?

Was Roberto or Mill Reef the only horse to beat Brigadier Gerard (in the 1972 Benson & Hedges Gold Cup)?

Was Cliff Thorburn playing Tony Meo or Terry Griffiths when scoring his maximum 147 in the 1983 world championships?

ANSWERS

SNOOKER BREAK (Page 132): 7: Cliff Thorburn; 1: Len Hutton; 7: Walter Donaldson; 1: Eddie Hide; 7: Tony Knowles.

Did Tony Sibson challenge Marvin Hagler or Tommy Hearns for the world middleweight title in 1983?

Which horse made Jenny Pitman the first woman to train a Grand National winner in 1983?

At which sport did Jim Fox, Adrian Parker and Danny Nightingale combine to win a gold medal in the 1976 Olympics?

With which FA Cup Final team did Charlie Cooke collect a winners' medal?

England batting master Tom Graveney started his career with which County?

And your final pot-the-black question: Which overseas player did Ray Reardon beat to win his sixth and last world title?

ANSWERS

Your Score

Running Total

There are seven questions here on ice skating. Award yourself two points for each correct answer.

Average score: 6   Greavsie: 8

1. Did Karina Richardson or Joanne Conway retain the British ladies' figure-skating championship in 1987?

2. In which English city did Jayne Torvill and Christopher Dean first start their partnership that led to world and Olympic championships?

3. Was Cecelia Colledge 11, 12 or 13 when she became Britain's youngest representative in an Olympics when skating in the 1932 Games?

4. Did Eric Heiden win four, five or six gold medals in the Olympic speed skating events in the 1980 Games at Lake Placid?

5. Who was a winner of an Olympic gold medal in the men's Olympic figure skating at the Games where East German Jan Hoffman was runner-up and American Charlie Tickner third?

6. What nationality was Ulrich Salchow, the originator of the 'salchow jump'—Norwegian, Swedish or Austrian?

7. Is it John Curry or Robin Cousins who is the only individual British skater to have won the grand slam of world, Olympic and European championships in the same year?

ANSWERS

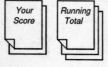

Your Score

Running Total

SNOOKER BREAK (Page 134): 7: Alison Fisher; 1: James Hunt; 7: Stephen Hendry; 1: Roberto; 7: Terry Griffiths.

*See how quickly you can identify
a star sportsman from the clues.*
Average score: 4 Greavsie: 6

For 12 points: Our mystery guest was born in Harrow, Middlesex, on March 23, 1929, and at 18 turned down a chance to compete in the 1948 Olympics.

For 10 points: He decided instead to concentrate on his medical studies and delayed his Olympic debut until the Helsinki Games in 1952.

For 8 points: Although one of the favourites, he could manage only a disappointing fourth place in the 1500 metres final.

For 6 points: Two years later he won gold medals in the Commonwealth and European championships.

For 4 points: In the Commonwealth Games mile final in Vancouver he beat his arch rival John Landy in a thrilling finish.

For 2 points: The highlight of his athletics career came on May 6, 1954, when he became the first man to run a mile in under four minutes. He has since been knighted.

ANSWERS

SNOOKER BREAK (Page 135): 2: Marvin Hagler; 3: Corbiere; 4: Modern Pentathlon; 5: Chelsea (1970); 6: Gloucestershire; 7: Perrie Mans.

Your Score

Running Total

You score two points for each correct answer in this round of show jumping questions
Average score: 4 Greavsie: 6

1. On which horse did Marion Coakes win a silver medal for Britain in the 1968 Olympics in Mexico?

a) Merely A Monarch; b) Stroller; c) The Rock

2. Who was the leading show jumper of the year for the third time in 1962 on Flanagan?

a) Pat Smythe; b) Alan Oliver; c) Ted Edgar

3. On which horse did Alwin Schockemöhle win the 1976 Olympic gold medal with a faultless performance?

a) Branch County; b) Warwick Rex; c) Alymony

4. David Broome won the King George V Gold Cup for the first of a record five times on which horse?

a) Sunsalve; b) Sportsman; c) Mister Softee

5. Who has won the Queen Elizabeth 11 Cup a record five times?

a) Ann Moore; b) Pat Moss; c) Elizabeth Edgar

6. Which rider has won a record five Olympic gold medals?

a) Hans-Günter Winkler; b) Raimondo d'Inzeo; c) Bill Steinkraus

7. On which horse did Nick Skelton clear 7ft 7in for a British record at Olympia in 1978?

a) Jimmy Brown; b) Wide Awake; c) Lastic

Your Score	Running Total

ANSWERS

NICE 'N' EASY (Page 136): 1: Joanne Conway; 2: Nottingham; 3: 11-years-old; 4: Five gold medals; 5: Robin Cousins (1980); 6: Swedish; 7: John Curry.

How well do you know the fastest men and women on earth? Two points for each correct answer to these who's who questions on sprinters past and present. **Average score: 4 Greavsie: 6**

1. Who was the first man to break the 10 seconds barrier for 100 metres with a wind-assisted 9.9 in California in 1963?

a) Jim Hines; b) Bob Hayes; c) Armin Hary

2. Who set what was then a world record for 100 metres at 9.93 seconds for 100 metres at Colorado Springs in 1983?

a) Don Quarrie; b) Mel Lattany; c) Calvin Smith

3. Who lowered the world's record for the women's 100 metres to 10.76 seconds in Zurich in 1984?

a) Marlies Göhr; b) Renate Stecher; c) Evelyn Ashford

4. Who won a record 14 AAA sprint titles and collected a bronze medal in the men's 100 metres at the 1952 Olympics?

a) Brian Shenton; b) Ken Jones; c) McDonald Bailey

5. Who ran a dead-heat with Allan Wells in the final of the Commonwealth Games 200 metres in Brisbane in 1982?

a) Mike McFarlane; b) Cameron Sharpe; c) Todd Bennett

6. Who twice clocked a world record 21.71 seconds for the women's 200 metres—first in 1979 and then in 1984?

a) Irena Szewinska; b) Bärbel Wöckel; c) Marita Koch

7. Who was runner-up when Ben Johnson won the 100 metres world title in a new world record in Rome in 1987?

a) Linford Christie; b) Carl Lewis; c) Silvio Leonard

ANSWERS

GUESS THE GUEST (Page 137): The mystery personality is Roger Bannister, the first man to break the four minute mile barrier.

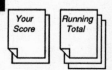

72 ON THE PISTE

Award yoursellf two points for each correct
answer to these questions about skiing.
Average score: 4 Greavsie: 4

1. Is World Cup slalom master Ingemar Stenmark Austrian, Swedish or Norwegian?

2. Has Annemarie Moser or Erika Hess won most World Cup titles in women's Alpine events?

3. Who won the 1956 giant slalom by a record margin of 6.2 seconds—Toni Sailer or Henri Oreiller?

4. Was Andreas Wenzel or Franz Klammer clocked at a record average speed of 102.82mph on his way to victory in the downhill race in the 1976 Olympics at Innsbruck?

5. Who failed by just 0.13 seconds to complete a hat-trick of gold medals in the women's downhill and slalom events in the 1976 Olympics—Rosi Mittermaier or Kathy Kreiner?

6. At which Olympics was Jean-Claude Killy named winner of the slalom after Karl Schranz had been disqualified—1964 or 1968?

7. Where were the 1988 Winter Olympics staged—Calgary, Grenoble or Lake Placid?

8. Is it permissible for a ski-racer to hold both hands on the same stick during the run—yes or no?

Your Score

Running Total

ANSWERS

JUST FOR SHOW (Page 138): 1. Stroller; 2. Pat Smythe; 3. Warwick Rex; 4. Sunsalve; 5. Elizabeth Edgar; 6. Hans-Günter Winkler; 7. Lastic.

HENRY COOPER

Award yourself one point for each question you can answer about former boxing champion Henry Cooper
Average score: 4 Greavsie: 6

1. What was the name of his amateur club?

2. How old was he when he won his first ABA championship?

3. In which weight division did he win his two ABA titles?

4. His twin brother is called George, but what was his ring name?

5. What was the name of Henry's wily old manager?

6. Who beat him in his first bid for a professional title—the Commonwealth Games heavyweight crown in 1957?

7. From whom did he take the British heavyweight championship in 1959?

8. Who knocked him out in five rounds when he challenged for the European title?

9. In which round did he knock down the then Cassius Clay at Wembley Stadium in 1963?

10. Who was his opponent in his last fight before his retirement in 1971?

ANSWERS

QUICK OFF THE MARK (Page 139): 1. Bob Hayes; 2. Calvin Smith; 3. Evelyn Ashford; 4. McDonald Bailey; 5. Mike McFarlane; 6. Marita Koch; 7. Carl Lewis.

Your Score

Running Total

74 THE OPEN ROUND

This is an 18-hole who's who of the winners of the British Open. There are four points for each correct answer, with a total of 72 points at stake. **Average score: 36 Greavsie: 40**

1 Who won the championship a record six times between 1896 and 1914?

a) James Braid; b) Harry Vardon; c) J.H. Taylor

2 Who is the American who completed four championship wins in 1929?

a) Walter Hagen; b) Bobby Jones; c) Gene Sarazen

3 Who carded a then record 65 on his way to victory at Sandwich in 1934?

a) Alf Padgham; b) Reg Whitcombe; c) Henry Cotton

4 Who was the American master who was the first post-war winner?

a) Byron Nelson; b) Frank Stranahan; c) Sam Snead

Your Score   Running Total

ANSWERS

ON THE PISTE (Page 140): 1. Swedish; 2. Annemarie Moser; 3. Toni Sailer; 4. Franz Klammer; 5. Rosi Mittermaier; 6. 1968; 7. Calgary; 8. No.

5 Who was the VIP who walked around the course supporting Henry Cotton in the 1948 Open?
   a) Winston Churchill; b) King George VI; c) Dwight Eisenhower

6 Who scored the first of his four victories after a play-off in 1949?
   a) Peter Thomson; b) Fred Daly; c) Bobby Locke

7 Who won in 1953 to complete a unique treble to go with his US Open and Masters titles?
   a) Ben Hogan; b) Doug Ford; c) Ed Furgol

8 Who was the second Australian after Peter Thomson to win the Open in 1960?
   a) Bruce Devlin; b) Kel Nagle; c) Norman von Nida

9 Who made a remarkable shot on his way to a 1961 win that's commemorated with a plaque?
   a) Arnold Palmer; b) Tony Lema; c) Phil Rodgers

10 Who completed his first Grand Slam by winning the 1966 championship?
   a) Gary Player; b) Tom Weiskopf; c) Jack Nicklaus

11 Who won the championship for the first time in 1967 at his 20th attempt?
   a) Roberto de Vicenzo; b) Dai Rees; c) Billy Casper

ANSWERS

HOW WELL D'YOU KNOW HENRY COOPER? (Page 141): 1. Bellingham ABC; 2. 17-years-old; 3. Light-heavyweight; 4. Jim Cooper; 5. Jim Wicks; 6. Joe Bygraves; 7. Brian London; 8. Ingemar Johansson; 9. Fourth Round; 10. Joe Bugner.

Your Score

Running Total

12 Who was runner-up when Tony Jacklin became the first British winner for 18 years?
a) Bob Charles; b) Max Faulkner; c) Brian Huggett

13 Who did Jack Nicklaus beat in a play-off for the title at St Andrews in 1970?
a) Dave Stockton; b) Ray Floyd; c) Doug Sanders

14 Who won the 100th Open to complete a hat-trick to go with the US and Canadian titles?
a) Hale Irwin; b) Lee Trevino; c) Tommy Aaron

15 Who won the first Open in which the large US ball was compulsory in 1974?
a) Gary Player; b) Johnny Miller; c) Charles Coody

16 Who beat Jack Nicklaus by one stroke in a classic head-to-head duel at Turnberry?
a) Lee Trevino; b) Tom Watson; c) Bill Rogers

17 Who became the first continental winner for 72 years at Royal Lytham in 1979?
a) Bernhard Langer; b) Seve Ballesteros; c) Manuel Pinero

18 Who went into the bunker at the 18th to let Nick Faldo in for his title win in 1987?
a) Bobby Clampett; b) Bobby Cole; c) Paul Azinger

ANSWERS

Your Score | Running Total

THE OPEN ROUND (Page 142): 1. Harry Vardon; 2. Walter Hagen; 3. Henry Cotton; 4. Sam Snead.

75 WHO DID WHAT?

There are 10 points at stake, one point for each correct answer. Each answer is a surname that starts with the same initial.
Average score: 5 Greavsie: 7

1. WHO was the first footballer to miss a penalty in an FA Cup Final at Wembley?

2. WHO was the Warwickshire opening batsman who scored 262 not out for England against the West Indies in 1974?

3. WHO is the boxer who took the world lightweight title from Jim Watt and won championships in two other weight divisions?

4. WHO played in Tottenham's double team and was top scorer for QPR when they won promotion from the Third Division?

5. WHO beat Martina Navratilova in the women's singles final in the US Open tennis championships in 1981?

6. WHO held the English long jump record for 33 years and was an Olympic gold medallist in another event in the 1924 Games?

7. WHO followed his father into the Ryder Cup team before starting a career as a golf commentator?

8. WHO took the world light-heavyweight title from J. B. Williamson and then lost it to Tommy Hearns?

9. WHO played for Spurs, Watford and West Brom and featured with Northern Ireland in the 1982 World Cup finals?

10. WHO was the Kent and England wicket-keeper who scored 37,248 runs during his career?

ANSWERS

THE OPEN ROUND (Page 143): 5. King George VI; 6. Bobby Locke; 7. Ben Hogan; 8. Kel Nagle; 9. Arnold Palmer; 10. Jack Nicklaus; 11. Roberto de Vicenzo.

Your Score

Running Total

76 MORE ODD ONES OUT

Who is the odd one out in each of the following six lists? We give you a little 'think hint' to help. Award yourself two points for each correct answer.

Average score: 6 Greavsie: 8

1. Test cricketers Wes Hall, Dennis Lillee, Freddie Trueman, Lance Gibbs, Imran Khan, Jeff Thomson, Frank Tyson, Michael Holding. *Think of the quickies.*

2. Tennis players Louise Brough, Maria Bueno, Christine Truman, Angela Mortimer, Althea Gibson, Ann Jones, Virginia Wade. *Think Wimbledon champions.*

3. Olympic medallists Eric Liddell, Albert Hill, Lord Burghley, David Hemery, Lynn Davies, Allan Wells, Sebastian Coe, Steve Ovett. *Think of track gold medallists.*

4. World boxing champions Ted 'Kid' Lewis, Sugar Ray Robinson, Emile Griffith, Joe 'Old Bones' Brown, John H. Stracey, Lloyd Honeyghan. *Think welterweights.*

5. Racehorses Never Say Die, Come to Daddy, Crepello, St Paddy, Sir Ivor, Nijinsky, Roberto, Empery, The Minstrel, Teenoso. *Think Lester Piggott Derby winners.*

6. Rugby stars Peter Wheeler, Colin Deans, John Pullin, Bobby Windsor, Dave Loveridge, Alain Paco, Andy Dalton. *Think international hookers.*

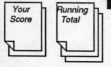

Your Score   Running Total

ANSWERS

THE OPEN ROUND (Page 144): 12. Bob Charles; 13. Tony Jacklin; 14. Lee Trevino; 15. Gary Player; 16. Tom Watson; 17. Severiano Ballesteros; 18. Paul Azinger.

77
ON A
PLATE

Here are 15 easy questions to help you boost your score. Award yourself a point for each correct answer, plus a one point bonus every time that you get three successive questions right.
Average score: 12 Greavsie: 16

1. Which west country football club is at home at Home Park?

2. In which Asian country did Mike Tyson defeat Tony Tubbs?

3. Which club did Graham Taylor manage before Aston Villa?

4. Which Middlesex batsman scored 13 centuries in 1947?

5. Who managed 1988 FA Cup winners Wimbledon?

6. Who was the first tennis player to complete the grand slam?

7. In which event was David Hemery an Olympic champion?

8. Who rode the winner of the 1988 Grand National?

9. With which sport do you associate the name Billy Boston?

10. On which cricket ground do Lancs usually play at home?

11. Judy Grinham specialised in which swimming stroke?

12. What nationality is middle-distance runner Lasse Viren?

13. Who had his first classic winner on Tap on Wood in 1979?

14. With which club did Jack Kelsey spend his entire career?

15. Mike Procter was an all-rounder with which County?

ANSWERS

WHO DID WHAT? (Page 145): 1. John Aldridge; 2. Dennis Amiss; 3. Alexis Arguello; 4. Les Allen; 5. Tracy Austin; 6. Harold Abrahams; 7. Peter Alliss; 8. Dennis Andries; 9. Gerry Armstrong; 10. Les Ames.

Your Score

Running Total

78

THE BOARD GAME

There are 180 points at stake in this all-sports quiz, with doubles and trebles to help you boost your score. You must answer the singles before you go on to the doubles and trebles.

Average score: 117 Greavsie: 128

 1. For 1 point, name one of the captains in the World Cup Final between West Germany and Holland in 1974.
Double your score if you can name them both. Treble your score if you can name the city that staged the game.

 2. For 1 point, name one of the three British boxers who have won the world middle-weight title since the war.
Double your score if you can name two. Treble your score if you can name all three.

 3. For 2 points, name one of the two darts masters who have won all of the four major championships.
Double your score if you can name them both. Treble your score if you can name the 1988 world champion.

Your Score *Running Total*

ANSWERS

MORE ODD ONES OUT (Page 146): 1. Lance Gibbs (a spin bowler); 2. Christine Truman (did not win a Wimbledon singles title); 3. Lynn Davies (won his gold medal in the long jump, not on the track); 4. Joe Brown (was world lightweight champion, not welterweight); 5. Come to Daddy (was not a Derby winner); 6. Dave Loveridge (a scrum-half, not a hooker).

4. For 1 point, name one of the 3 managers who guided Celtic, Manchester United and Liverpool to their first European Cup wins.
Double your score if you can name two. Treble your score if you can name all three.

 5. For 2 points, name two of the four Americans who have won the men's Wimbledon singles title since 1970.
Double your score if you can name three. Treble your score if you can name all four.

 6. For 2 points, name one of the two counties for whom England off-spinner Geoff Miller has played.
Double your score if you can name them both. Treble your score if you can give his nickname.

 7. For 2 points, name one of the medallists in the men's 100 metres track final in the 1980 Olympics.
Double your score if you can name two. Treble your score if you can name all three.

 8. For 2 points, name one of the three clubs Stanley Matthews played against in FA Cup Finals at Wembley.
Double your score if you can name two. Treble your score if you can name all three.

ANSWERS

ON A PLATE (Page 147): 1. Plymouth Argyle; 2. Japan; 3. Watford; 4. Bill Edrich; 5. Bobby Gould; 6. Donald Budge; 7. 400 metres hurdles; 8. Brendan Powell; 9. Rugby League; 10. Old Trafford; 11. Backstroke; 12. Finnish; 13. Steve Cauthen; 14. Arsenal; 15. Gloucestershire.

Your Score

Running Total

9. For 2 points, name two of the five boxers Rocky Marciano defeated in world heavyweight championship contests.

Double your score if you can name three. Treble your score if you can name four or more.

 10. For 2 points, name one of the three major races that Willie Carson won on Troy during the 1979 season.

Double your score if you can name two. Treble your score if you can name all three.

 11. For 2 points, name one of the four British marathon runners who have won an Olympic silver medal.

Double your score if you can name two. Treble your score if you can name three or more.

 12. For 2 points, name one of the two batsmen who shared a record sixth wicket stand of 215 for England against Australia in 1977.

Double your score if you can name them both. Treble your score if you can name the ground on which they did it.

 13. For 2 points, name three of the seven clubs for which centre-forward Tony Hateley played during his League career.

Double your score if you can name four. Treble your score if you can name five or more.

| Your Score | Running Total |

ANSWERS

THE BOARD GAME (Page 148): 1. Franz Beckenbauer, Johan Cruyff, Munich; 2. Randolph Turpin, Terry Downes, Alan Minter; 3. John Lowe, Eric Bristow, Bob Anderson.

14. For 2 points, name the Rugby player who kicked five penalties and three conversions for Scotland against England in 1985.
Double your score if you can say where the game was played. Treble your score if you can give the final score.

 15. For 2 points, name the first British boxer to win the world light-heavyweight championship in the post-war period.
Double your score if you can name the fighter he beat for the title. Treble your score if you name the year he won it.

 16. For 2 points, name the one player who appeared in all of Liverpool's European Champions Cup final teams.
Double your score if you name his first club. Treble your score if you give the year of his first European Cup final.

 17. For 2 points, name one of the two American golfers involved in a play-off for the US Masters title in 1982.
Double your score if you name them both. Treble your score if you can say at which hole the play-off was won.

 18. For 2 points, name the team which won the County Cricket Championship in the 1986 season.
Double your score if you name their captain. Treble your score if you can say who topped their batting averages.

ANSWERS

THE BOARD GAME (Page 149): 4. Jock Stein (Celtic), Matt Busby (Manchester United), Bob Paisley (Liverpool); 5. Stan Smith, Jimmy Connors, Arthur Ashe, John McEnroe; 6. Derbyshire, Essex, Dusty; 7. Allan Wells, Silvio Leonard, Petar Petrov; 8. Manchester United, Newcastle United, Bolton Wanderers.

 Your Score

 Running Total

19. For 2 points, name one of the two riders who tied for the 1981-82 National Hunt Jockeys' Championship.

Double your score if you can name them both. Treble your score if you can name how many winners each rode.

20. For 2 points, name one of the two teams that met in the 1988 Rugby League Premier Championship final.

Double your score if you can name them both. Treble your score if you can give the result.

21. For 2 points, name two of the four fighters George Foreman met in world heavyweight title fights.

Double your score if you can name three of them. Treble your score if you can name all four.

22. For 4 points, name four of the Wimbledon team that beat Liverpool 1-0 in the 1988 FA Cup Final at Wembley.

Double your score if you can name six. Treble your score if you can name eight or more.

23. For 26 points, name eight of the 11 cities that have staged the Summer Olympics since the war.

You hit the **BULLSEYE** for another 25 points if you can name all eleven of the cities.

ANSWERS

Your Score

Running Total

THE BOARD GAME (Page 150): 9. Jersey Joe Walcott, Roland LaStarza, Ezzard Charles, Don Cockell, Archie Moore; 10. Epsom Derby, Irish Sweeps Derby, King George VI and Queen Elizabeth Diamond Stakes; 11. Sam Ferris (1932), Ernest Harper (1936), Tom Richards (1948), Basil Heatley (1964); 12. Geoff Boycott, Alan Knott, Trent Bridge; 13. Notts County, Aston Villa, Chelsea, Liverpool, Coventry, Birmingham, Oldham.

Each of the
questions relate
to sporting
books. Two
points for each
correct answer.
**Average score: 6
Greavsie: 8**

79 SPORTS BOOKSHELF

1. Who wrote the best selling novel about professional heavy-weight boxing called *The Harder They Fall?*

a) Ernest Hemingway; b) Norman Mailer; c) Bud Schulberg

2. Which former Eire international footballer co-wrote a book with Peter Ball that was called *Only A Game?*

a) Johnny Giles; b) Eamonn Dunphy; c) Paddy Mulligan

3. Which sport features in *Meat on the Hoof* by Gary Shaw?

a) American football; b) Boxing; c) Wrestling

4. *Gents and Players* was the best-selling book published in 1986 by which leading sportswriter?

a) Ian Wooldridge; b) Frank Keating; c) Patrick Collins

5. Which former England skipper had a book published in 1986 called *Starting With Grace?*

a) Peter May; b) Bob Willis; c) Mike Denness

6. What was the title of Len Shackleton's famous autobiography?

a) Clown Prince of Soccer; b) The Roker Joker; c) Chuckle Boots

7. Which former England batting master had a book published in 1988 called *The Ten Greatest Test Teams?*

a) Colin Cowdrey; b) Denis Compton; c) Tom Graveney

8. Who was the footballer who had an autobiography published called *Man for All Seasons?*

a) Steve Perryman; b) Terry Paine; c) Peter Shilton

ANSWERS

THE BOARD GAME (Page 151): 14. Gavin Hastings, Murrayfield, 33-6; 15. Freddie Mills, Gus Lesnevich, 1948; 16. Phil Neal, Northampton, 1977; 17. Craig Stadler, Dan Pohl, The first hole in the sudden-death play-off; 18. Essex, Keith Fletcher, Allan Border.

80 THE NAME GAME

EACH clue leads to a well-known name. Put the initials in the appropriate squares to identify a sports star: Two points for each correct answer, plus a bonus of ten points for completing the main name.

Average score: 16 Greavsie: 20

1	2	3	4	5			
6	7	8	9	10	11	12	13

2 & 8	He collected a World Cup winners' medal in 1978 and joined Blackburn from Spurs.
4 & 7	This former Liverpool winger was known as Little Bamber at Anfield.
10 & 5	The great Russian goalkeeper who was nicknamed the Man in Black.
3	Nino, who was an Olympic and world professional boxing champion in the 1960s.
11 & 13	He was Northern Ireland's centre-half and captain before managing Arsenal.
9 & 1	This athlete won the 400 metres European championship for Britain in 1986.
6 & 2	A cricketing all-rounder whose brother is an England Rugby Union international.

Your Score

Running Total

ANSWERS

81 THE FIVE STAR TEST

Award yourself one point for each correct identification in this five-star test.

Average score: 13 Greavsie: 17

1. Which five of these boxers has held a version of the world heavyweight title?—Tony Tubbs, Gerrie Coetzee, Gerry Cooney, Mike Weaver, Earnie Shavers, Jimmy Young, Mike Dokes, Ron Lyle, John Tate, Marvin Frazier.

2. Which five of these footballers has scored from the penalty spot in an FA Cup Final: Geoff Hurst, Danny Blanchflower, Ronnie Allen, Phil Neal, Alan Sunderland, Kevin Reeves, Ray Wilkins, Graeme Sharp, Glenn Hoddle, Arnold Muhren.

3. Which five of these cricketers has captained England in Test cricket?—Norman Yardley, Godfrey Evans, Denis Compton, Tom Graveney, Colin Cowdrey, Brian Statham, Tony Lewis, John Snow, Keith Fletcher, Allan Lamb.

4. Which five of these Rugby players has been a Welsh international fly-half: Cliff Morgan, Gwyn Evans, David Watkins, Graham Price, Phil Bennett, Jeff Squire, Bobby Windsor, Barry John, Cliff Ashton, Alun Pask.

5. Which five of these athletes did not win Olympic gold medals: Harrison Dillard, McDonald Bailey, Chris Brasher, Roger Bannister, Rod Milburn, Ron Clarke, Gordon Pirie, Dave Wottle, David Bedford, Murray Halberg.

ANSWERS

SPORTBOOKSHELF (Page 153): 1. Bud Schulberg; 2. Eamonn Dunphy; 3. American Football; 4. Frank Keating; 5. Bob Willis; 6. Clown Prince of Soccer; 7. Tom Graveney; 8. Steve Perryman.

Your Score

Running Total

Simply answer true or false to the following statements.
Two points for each correct answer.
Average score: 8   Greavsie: 8

82 TRUE OR FALSE?

 1. Sir Stanley Matthews was the son of a prominent professional boxer.

 2. Golfer Peter Alliss was born in Berlin and weighed 15 pounds at birth.

 3. Nobby Stiles missed a 1966 World Cup finals match after losing his contact lenses.

 4. Ex-world boxing champion Jim Watt plays professional-standard 'blues' guitar.

 5. Keith Miller was once reported to the umpire for polishing the ball with Brylcreem.

 6. Bran Clough used to drive the team coach when he was manager at Hartlepool.

ANSWERS

 Your Score Running Total

THE NAME GAME (Page 154): BOBBY CHARLTON (Osvaldo Ardiles, Brian Hall, Lev Yashin, Nino Benvenuti, Terry Neill, Roger Black, Chris Old).

156

HOW WELL D'YOU KNOW...?
GARETH EDWARDS

Award yourself one point for each question you can answer about Gareth Edwards
Average score: 4 Greavsie: 6

1. At which famous English sports school was he a pupil?

2. Which Soccer club offered him a place on their groundstaff?

3. With which Rugby club side was he playing when he got his first call into the Welsh team?

4. How many caps did he win —a record for a Welsh scrum-half?

5. Against which team did he make his first and last appearance for Wales?

6. Who was his fly-half partner in his first international?

7. With which player does he share the record of 20 tries for Wales in international matches?

8. Who was his fly-half partner in 23 internationals, in five matches with the British Lions and also at club level?

9. On which ground did he score a classical try for the Barbarians against the All Blacks in 1973?

10. In which year did he play his final competitive match?

ANSWERS

THE FIVE-STAR TEST (Page 155): 1. Tubbs, Coetzee, Weaver, Dokes, Tate; 2. Blanchflower, Allen, Reeves, Hoddle, Muhren; 3. Yardley, Graveney, Cowdrey, Lewis, Fletcher; 4. Morgan, Watkins, Bennett, John, Ashton; 5. Bailey, Bannister, Clarke, Pirie, Bedford.

Your Score | Running Total

Do you know your way around the sports world? This will test you. One point each time you know where you are. **Average score: 5 Greavsie: 7**

Where are you when you're watching...

1. League football at the Racecourse Ground.

2. West Indies playing England in a Test match at Sabina Park.

3. The All Blacks against the British Lions at Athletic Park.

4. A motor racing Grand Prix at the Interlagos circuit.

5. World championship boxing at the Trump Plaza.

6. The World Matchplay Golf Championship in Surrey.

7. An athletics meeting in the Meadowbank Stadium.

8. The Tigers playing baseball in their hometown.

9. A race meeting where the Eclipse Stakes is being staged.

10. United States Open tennis at Flushing Meadow.

11. Red Star playing a European Cup match in their hometown.

12. A cricket match in the land of Derek Pringle's birth.

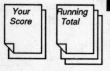

Your Score   Running Total

ANSWERS

TRUE OR FALSE (Page 156): 1. True (He was known as the Fighting Barber of Hanley); 2. True (His father, Percy, was a resident professional in Berlin); 3. False; 4. True; 5. False; 6. True.

See how quickly you can identify a sports personality from the clues.
Average score: 6 Greavsie: 8

For 12 points: Our mystery guest was born in London in 1958, and he first came to international prominence in his sport when competing in the 1976 Montreal Olympics.

For 10 points: In 1978 he won the first of three successive Commonwealth Games gold medals.

For 8 points: His mother was Scottish and his father was born in Nigeria.

For 6 points: He became Olympic champion in Moscow in 1980 and two years later won the European title.

For 4 points: A magnificent all-rounder, he retained his Olympic title in Los Angeles in 1984 despite strong competition from his West German rivals.

For 2 points: He has been a world record holder in the decathlon, and his only defeat in a major championship in nine years came in the 1987 world championships when he was not 100 per cent fit.

ANSWERS

HOW WELL D'YOU KNOW GARETH EDWARDS? (Page 157): 1. Millfield School, Somerset; 2. Swansea Town (now City); 3. Cardiff; 4. 53; 5. France; 6. David Watkins; 7. Gerald Davies; 8. Barry John; 9. Cardiff Arms Park; 10. 1978.

Your Score

Running Total

86

Just answer 'yes' or 'no' to these football questions. One point for each correct answer and a bonus of one each time you get three right in succession.
Average score: 9 Greavsie: 15

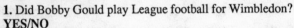

1. Did Bobby Gould play League football for Wimbledon?
YES/NO

2. Was Neil Webb ever on Reading's books?
YES/NO

3. Did Liverpool use both their substitutes in the 1988 FA Cup Final?
YES/NO

4. Has Willie Miller won more Scotland caps than John Greig?
YES/NO

5. Do Oldham Athletic play their home games at Edgeley Park?
YES/NO

6. Did Alan Ball win an FA Cup winners' medal with Everton?
YES/NO

7. Did Gordon Strachan start his playing career with Aberdeen?
YES/NO

8. Did Italy win the European Championship in 1984?
YES/NO

9. Do Blackburn Rovers play their home matches at Turf Moor?
YES/NO

10. Did Denis Law ever score a goal in an FA Cup Final?
YES/NO

11. Have Tottenham had a home ground other than White Hart Lane?
YES/NO

12. Was John Hollins capped by England during his playing career?
YES/NO

13. Did Clive Allen play any League matches for Arsenal?
YES/NO

14. Has Sammy McIlroy won more Irish caps than George Best?
YES/NO

15. Did Peter Beardsley score for England in the 1986 World Cup finals?
YES/NO

ANSWERS

GOING PLACE (Page 158): 1. Wrexham; 2. Kingston, Jamaica; 3. Wellington; 4. Brazil; 5. Atlantic City; 6. Wentworth; 7. Edinburgh; 8. Detroit; 9. Sandown; 10. New York; 11. Belgrade; 12. Kenya.

87

ROUNDERS

The sports puzzle that will have you going in circles

Each clue leads to a familiar sports word or surname. The LAST letter of each word or name is the FIRST letter of the next. Two points for each correct answer and a 5-point bonus if you complete the circle.
Average score: 9
Greavsie: 11

1	He nodded the winning FA Cup Final goal for the Dons (7).
2	The country where Ali and Foreman rumbled in the jungle (5).
3	A high-flying two shots under par at a golf hole (5).
4	East Germany's golden girl in Montreal's Olympic pool (5).
5	Allan, who opened in style for the 1950 West Indians (3).
6	He was the Kent and England wicket-keeper in the 1950s (5).

ANSWERS

GUESS THE GUEST (Page 159): The mystery personality is Daley Thompson, the king of the decathletes.

Your Score

Running Total

Each clue leads to a sports personality who does things by the left. Two points for each one that you can identify
Average score: 14 Greavsie: 18

88

BY THE LEFT

1. She was a finalist in world table tennis championships and won a Wimbledon title.

2. He is the only left hander to have won the British Open Golf Championship.

3. This footballer was famed and feared for his left foot shooting and he played for Real Madrid and the 'Magical Magyars' team of the 1950s.

4. He challenged Muhammad Ali for the world title and won the British heavyweight championship with his southpaw punches.

5. An all-rounder, his left arm pace bowling made him an ideal successor to Ray Lindwall as Australia's chief strike bowler.

6. This Irishman has played for Arsenal and West Ham and in Italy and his left foot is known as 'The Claw.'

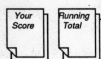

Your Score   Running Total

ANSWERS

ON THE BALL (Page 160): 1. No; 2. Yes; 3. Yes, 4. Yes; 5. No (Oldham play at Boundary Park, Stockport at Edgeley Park); 6. No (he collected a runners-up medal in 1968); 7. No (Dundee); 8. No (France); 9. No (Blackburn play at Ewood Park, Burnley at Turf Moor); 10. Yes; 11. Yes; 12. Yes (1 cap); 13. Yes; 14. No. 15. Yes.

7. She won her first Wimbledon singles championship when beating Chris Evert in 1982.

8. He has completely dominated the men's English open table tennis championship since 1976.

9. The Leicestershire stylist who scored more than a thousand Test runs in 1982.

10. This England international darts player is usually the 'man in black' on the oche.

11. The Londoner who teams up with Steve Davis in the world snooker doubles championships.

12. After making his biting tackles, he usually passed with his left foot for Leeds United.

13. The 'Dartford Destroyer' who won a Lonsdale Belt outright in the lightweight division in 1963.

14. He stroked his way to 39,790 runs for Surrey and England between 1956 and 1978.

15. This stalwart of Britain's Davis Cup team is now a regular at the BBC-tv microphone.

ANSWERS

ROUNDERS (Page 161): 1. (Lawrie) Sanchez; 2. Zaire; 3. Eagle; 4. (Kornelia) Ender; 5. (Allan) Rae; 6. (Godfrey) Evans.

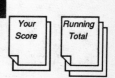

Your Score   Running Total

89

BIG FIGHT QUIZ

Seconds out for a test of your knowledge of world heavyweight champions. There are 15 rounds of questions. Award yourself four points for each correct answer.

Average score: 32
Greavsie: 36

Who did Muhammad Ali knock out in round one of his first world title defence?

a) Cleveland Williams; b) Sonny Liston; c) Bob Foster

Who stopped Ken Norton in two rounds of a world title fight in 1974?

a) Muhammad Ali; b) Joe Frazier; c) George Foreman

Who knocked out Billy Miske in three rounds in his first defence of the world crown?

a) Jack Johnson; b) Jess Willard; c) Jack Dempsey

Who was the only boxer to win the title on a foul in round 4 against Jack Sharkey?

a) Primo Carnera; b) Max Baer; c) Max Schmeling

ANSWERS

Your Score

Running Total

BY THE LEFT (162): 1. Ann Jones; 2. Bob Charles; 3. Ferenc Puskas; 4. Richard Dunn; 5. Alan Davidson; 6. Liam Brady.

BIG FIGHT QUIZ

 **Who knocked out Archie Moore in five rounds to win the title in 1956?**

a) Floyd Patterson; b) Jersey Joe Walcott; c) Marvin Hart

 **Who was stopped in 6 rounds when fighting for the world title in his pro debut?**

a) Tom McNeeley; b) Pete Rademacher; c) Lee Oma

 **Who stopped Scott LeDoux in seven rounds of a world title defence in 1980?**

a) Mike Dokes; b) Mike Weaver; c) Larry Holmes

 **Who knocked out Billy Conn in eight rounds of a return world title fight?**

a) James J. Braddock; b) Joe Louis; c) Jack Sharkey

 **Who did Rocky Marciano stop in nine rounds in his final title defence?**

a) Archie Moore; b) Don Cockell; c) Ezzard Charles

ANSWERS

BY THE LEFT (Page 163): 7. Martina Navratilova; 8. Desmond Douglas; 9. David Gower; 10. Alan Glazier; 11. Tony Meo; 12. Norman Hunter; 13. Dave Charnley; 14. John Edrich; 15. Mark Cox.

 Your Score

 Running Total

BIG FIGHT QUIZ

 **Who did Larry Holmes stop in 10 rounds in 1985?**

a) Renaldo Snipes; b) Tex Cobb; c) David Bey

 **Who did Tim Witherspoon stop in 11 rounds in a world title defence in 1986?**

a) Frank Bruno; b) Tony Tubbs; c) Greg Page

 **Who floored Jack Johnson before being ko'd in the 12th?**

a) Tommy Burns; b) Stanley Ketchel; c) Marvin Hart

 **Who ko'd Jersey Joe Walcott in the 13th to win the title?**

a) Ingemar Johansson; b) Rocky Marciano; c) Joey Maxim

 **Who did Bob Fitzsimmons ko in the 14th to win the title?**

a) James J. Corbett; b) John L. Sullivan; c) James J. Jeffries

 **Who did Muhammad Ali stop in the 15th round in 1975?**

a) Ron Lyle; b) Leon Spinks; c) Chuck Wepner

Your Score | Running Total

ANSWERS

166

There have been 13 World Cup finals, first for the Jules Rimet Trophy and then—from 1974—for the FIFA World Cup. There are four points for each correct answer to these questions on World Cup Finals

Average score: 48
Greavsie: 56

1. In which country were the first World Cup Finals staged?
a) Brazil; b) Argentina; c) Uruguay

2. Who were the first winners?
a) Brazil; b) Argentina; c) Uruguay

3. Italy beat which country after extra-time in the second Final?
a) Austria; b) Czechoslovakia; c) Spain

4. In which city was the Final?
a) Turin; b) Rome; c) Milan

5. In which country were the third World Cup Finals staged?
a) France; b) Chile; c) Germany

6. Who did Italy beat in the Final?
a) Hungary; b) Rumania; c) Poland

ANSWERS

BIG FIGHT QUIZ (Page 165): 5. Floyd Patterson; 6. Pete Rademacher; 7. Larry Holmes; 8. Joe Louis; 9. Archie Moore.

Your Score

Running Total

7. What was the world record attendance for the deciding match?
a) 175,000; b) 200,000; c) 225,000

8. Who beat Brazil in the Final?
a) Italy; b) Uruguay; c) Argentina

9. Who scored West Germany's winning goal in the Final?
a) Fritz Walter; b) Helmut Rahn; c) Otto Mai

10. Which team were runners-up?
a) Hungary; b) Switzerland; c) Yugoslavia

11. How old was Pele when making his World Cup debut for Brazil?
a) 16; b) 17; c) 18

12. Which team were runners-up?
a) Belgium; b) Sweden; c) France

13. Who replaced the injured Pele and scored in the Final?
a) Didi; b) Garrincha; c) Amarildo

14. Who were the runners-up?
a) Bulgaria; b) Paraguay; c) Czechoslovakia

Your Score

Running Total

15. What nationality was the referee for the Final at Wembley?
a) Belgian; b) Italian; c) Swiss
16. Who captained the runners-up?
a) Willi Schulz; b) Uwe Seeler; c) Ziggi Held

17. Who collected the Jules Rimet Trophy that Brazil won outright?
a) Carlos Alberto; b) Pele; c) Gerson
18. Which team were runners-up?
a) Argentina; b) Holland; c) Italy

19. Who scored a first minute penalty for Holland in the Final?
a) Neeskens; b) Cruyff; c) Rensenbrink
20. Who netted the winning goal?
a) Beckenbauer; b) Breitner; c) Muller

21. Who scored two goals against Holland in the Final?
a) Luque; b) Kempes; c) Bertoni
22. Who was Argentina's captain?
a) Passarella; b) Ardiles; c) Tarantini

ANSWERS

WORLD CUP FINALS (Page 167): 1. Uruguay (Montevideo); 2. Uruguay; 3. Czechoslovakia; 4. Rome; 5. France; 6. Hungary.

Your Score

Running Total

23. Who scored Italy's first goal in the Final?
a) Tardelli; b) Altobelli; c) Rossi
24. Who captained the winners?
a) Cabrini; b) Zoff; c) Gentile

25. Who scored Argentina's third victory-clinching goal?
a) Burruchaga; b) Maradona; c) Valdano
26. Which team were runners-up?
a) France; b) Poland; c) West Germany

IN SAFE KEEPING

Name the goalkeepers of the following World Cup winning teams (2 points for each correct answer):

1: Brazil (1958 and 1962)
2: England (1966)
3: Brazil (1970)
4: West Germany (1974)
5: Argentina (1978)

ANSWERS

WORLD CUP FINALS (Page 168): 7. 200,000; 8. Uruguay; 9. Helmut Rahn; 10. Hungary; 11. 17 years old; 12. Sweden; 13. Amarildo; 14. Czechoslovakia.

91
HARK WHO'S TALKING

There are quotes on this page from six famous sports personalities. Score two points for each that you correctly identify.
Average score: 6 Greavsie: 8

1. "I had studied where Aldridge put his penalties on video, and I was confident when I dived to my left that I would be able to save it. I did not give a second's thought to the fact that it had never been done in an FA Cup Final before."
a) Neville Southall; b) Steve Ogrizovic; c) Dave Beasant

2. "I work up a hatred against all batsmen. That way I get really fired up and mean. I wouldn't fancy being the bloke facing me."
a) Harold Larwood; b) Jeff Thomson; c) Charlie Griffith

3. "There's not a single guy on this planet who can beat me."
a) Mike Tyson; b) Marvin Hagler; c) Tommy Hearns

4. "Until I was ten I was a rather sickly child with little strength Any kid on the block could have taken liberties with me. I was always going to be the one who had sand kicked in his face."
a) Daley Thompson; b) Arnold Schwarzenegger; c) Frank Bruno

5. "I'm so competitive I can't even allow my son to beat me at tiddlywinks. That's just the way I am."
a) Jimmy Connors; b) Bryan Robson; c) Ian Botham

6. "There are two things that no man will admit he can't do well: drive and make love."
a) Stirling Moss; b) James Hunt; c) Niki Lauda

ANSWERS

WORLD CUP FINALS (Page 169): 15. Swiss (Georg Dienst); 16. Uwe Seeler; 17. Carlos Alberto; 18. Italy; 19. Johan Neeskens; 20. Gerd Muller; 21. Mario Kempes; 22. Daniel Passarella.

Your Score

Running Total

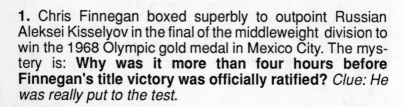

92 SPORTS SLEUTH

Here are four sporting mysteries for you to solve. Award yourself four points for each correct answer.
Average score: 8 Greavsie: 8

1. Chris Finnegan boxed superbly to outpoint Russian Aleksei Kisselyov in the final of the middleweight division to win the 1968 Olympic gold medal in Mexico City. The mystery is: **Why was it more than four hours before Finnegan's title victory was officially ratified?** *Clue: He was really put to the test.*

2. Bobby Locke, four times British Open golf champion, struck a ball to the heart of the green at the short 12th hole in the Irish Open at Dublin in 1936. It looked the perfect shot. The mystery is: **Why was Locke unable to find his ball when he got to the green?** *Clue: It was enough to drive Locke up the pole!*

3. Derek Randall was voted Man of the Match after scoring 174 for England against Australia in the Centenary Test in 1977—yet he had 'walked' after being given out earlier in his innings. The mystery is: **Why was Randall recalled after the umpire had held up a finger?** *Clue: Rodney Marsh played a part in the decision.*

4. Colchester goalkeeper Graham Smith had a pre-match ritual during which he kicked the foot of each of his goalposts. The mystery is: **Why did his superstition delay a League match?** *Clue: He could not save himself!*

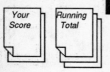

Your Score | Running Total

ANSWERS

WORLD CUP FINALS (Page 170): 23. Paolo Rossi; 24. Dino Zoff; 25. Burruchaga; 26. West Germany. In Safe Keeping: 1. Gylmar; 2. Gordon Banks; 3. Felix; 4. Sepp Maier; 5. Ubaldo Fillol.

HOW WELL D'YOU KNOW...?
JOHN McENROE

Award yourself one point for each question you can answer about John McEnroe
 Average score: 5 Greavsie: 7

1. In which European country was he born?

2. In which year did he become the first qualifier to reach the Wimbledon semi-finals?

3. How old was he when he reached his first Wimbledon singles final?

4. Which rival New Yorker did he beat when winning his first US Open final in 1979?

5. Who did he beat when winning his first Wimbledon singles title?

6. Which of his doubles partners later became his manager?

7. Name the Swede who beat him three times on different surfaces in 1983 when he was ranked No 1.

8. Who did he meet in the 1982 and 1984 Wimbledon finals, losing the first and winning the second match?

9. How long did it take him to win the 1983 Wimbledon final—65, 75 or 85 minutes?

10. Which film actress did he marry?

ANSWERS

HARK WHO'S TALKING (Page 171): 1. Dave Beasant; 2. Jeff Thomson; 3. Mike Tyson; 4. Arnold Schwarzenegger; 5. Ian Botham; 6. Stirling Moss.

Your Score

Running Total

THE CAPTAINS' TABLE

There are two points for each correct answer in this who's who of captains.
Average score: 10
Greavsie: 12

1. Who played at Wembley with Leicester City and captained the 1976 Southampton FA Cup winning team?

2. Who did Peter May succeed as skipper of the Surrey side that dominated the County championship in the 1950s?

3. Who is the blond flank forward who captained France a record 30 times between 1979 and 1984?

4. Who captained the Celtic team that became the first British club to win the European Cup in 1967?

5. Who captained England's cricket team on their infamous 'Bodyline' tour of Australia?

6. Who skippered the Wigan team that beat Halifax in the 1988 Rugby League Challenge Cup Final at Wembley?

7. Who was the English-born footballer who captained Scotland's World Cup squad in the 1978 finals?

8. Who set an all-time record in the world of cricket by leading his country in 74 Test matches?

9. Who skippered the Wimbledon team that beat Liverpool in the 1988 FA Cup Final at Wembley?

Your Score

Running Total

ANSWERS

SPORTS SLEUTH (Page 172): 1. It took Finnegan more than four hours to produce a urine sample for the drugs test; 2. The ball was trapped in the furled flag; 3. Rodney Marsh sportingly informed the umpire that he had not made a clean catch; 4. As Smith kicked the foot of one of the goal-posts the crossbar fell on his head.

Untangle the letters in each of the sections to identify famous sports personalities. Award yourself four points for each correct identification.

Average score: 8 Greavsie: 8

1. Clue: He could have you jumping to conclusions.

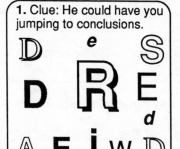

2. Clue: One half of a great double act!

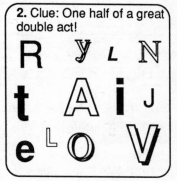

3. Clue: A four-times Olympic gold medallist

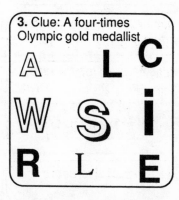

4. Clue: A batsman who bristles for England.

ANSWERS

HOW WELL D'YOU KNOW JOHN McENROE? (Page 173): 1. West Germany; 2. 1977; 3. 21-years-old; 4. Vitas Gerulaitis; 5. Bjorn Borg; 6. Peter Fleming; 7. Mats Wilander; 8. Jimmy Connors; 9. 85 minutes; 10. Tatum O'Neal.

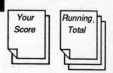

Your Score — *Running Total*

COMPUTER RATINGS

On the following six pages you can match your sports knowledge and opinions against a computer. We have fed into a computer facts and figures (and added personal feelings) on the 12 top performers in several sports. We have listed them in alphabetical order. All you have to do is number the sports stars in the order that you rate them, taking skill, achievement, experience and physical attributes into account. For instance, in the boxing if you consider Muhammad Ali to have been No.1 put a figure '1' in the box alongside his name, then a '2' alongside your second-rated boxer and rate them all from 1-12. Then compare your list with the computer rating answers and award yourself one point each time your rating matches that of the computer.

ANSWERS

THE CAPTAINS' TABLE (Page 174): 1. Peter Rodrigues; 2. Stuart Surridge;
3. Jean-Pierre Rives; 4. Billy McNeill; 5. Douglas Jardine; 6. Shaun Edwards;
7. Bruce Rioch; 8. Clive Lloyd; 9. Dave Beasant.

COMPUTER RATINGS BOXING

There are 12 all-time great world heavyweight champions listed below in alphabetical order. See if your ratings of them match the computer. Award yourself one point each time your rating is the same.

Average score: 6 Greavsie: 7

1 Jack Dempsey

2 George Foreman

3 Joe Frazier

4 Larry Holmes

5 James J. Jeffries

6 Jack Johnson

7 Sonny Liston

8 Joe Louis

9 Rocky Marciano

10 Muhammad Ali

11 Gene Tunney

12 Mike Tyson

ANSWERS

SPORTSTANGLE (Page 175): 1. Eddie Edwards; 2. Jayne Torvill; 3. Carl Lewis; 4. Mike Gatting.

Your Score   Running Total

There are 12 post-war world middleweight champions listed below in alphabetical order. See if your ratings of them match the computer. Award yourself one point each time your rating is the same.

Average score: 5 Greavsie: 6

1 Carmen Basilio

2 Nino Benvenuti

3 Gene Fullmer

4 Rocky Graziano

5 Emile Griffith

6 Marvin Hagler

7 Jake La Motta

8 Carlos Monzon

9 Sugar Ray Robinson

10 Dick Tiger

11 Rodrigo Valdez

12 Tony Zale

ANSWERS

Your Score

Running Total

The computer ratings for these world middleweight champions are on Page 180.

COMPUTER RATINGS CRICKET

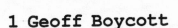

There are 12 outstanding post-war opening Test batsmen listed below in alphabetical order. See if your ratings of them match the computer. Award yourself one point each time your rating is the same.

Average score: 4 Greavsie: 4

1 Geoff Boycott

2 Chris Broad

3 John Edrich

4 Sunil Gavaskar

5 Graham Gooch

6 Gordon Greenidge

7 Hanif Mohammad

8 Len Hutton

9 Bill Lawry

10 Barry Richards

11 Bobby Simpson

12 Glenn Turner

ANSWERS

COMPUTER RATINGS, BOXING (Page 177): 1. Joe Louis; 2. Muhammad Ali; 3. Rocky Marciano; 4. Mike Tyson; 5. Jack Johnson; 6. Gene Tunney; 7. Jack Dempsey; 8. Larry Holmes; 9. James J.Jeffries; 10. George Foreman; 11. Sonny Liston; 12. Joe Frazier.

Your Score

Running Total

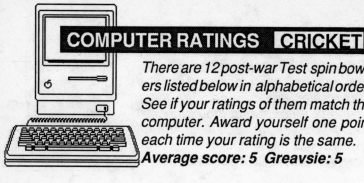

COMPUTER RATINGS ▮CRICKET▮

There are 12 post-war Test spin bowlers listed below in alphabetical order. See if your ratings of them match the computer. Award yourself one point each time your rating is the same.
Average score: 5 Greavsie: 5

1 Abdul Qadir

2 Bishen Bedi

3 Richie Benaud

4 Chandrasekhar

5 John Emburey

6 Lance Gibbs

7 Jim Laker

8 Tony Lock

9 Erapally Prasanna

10 Sonny Ramadhin

11 Hugh Tayfield

12 Derek Underwood

Your Score

Running Total

ANSWERS

COMPUTER RATINGS, BOXING (Page 178): 1. Sugar Ray Robinson; 2. Carlos Monzon; 3. Marvin Hagler; 4. Tony Zale; 5. Jake La Motta; 6. Emile Griffith; 7. Dick Tiger; 8. Nino Benvenuti; 9. Gene Fullmer; 10. Rocky Graziano; 11. Carmen Basilio; 12. Rodrigo Valdez.

COMPUTER RATINGS TENNIS

There are 12 outstanding post-war left-handed men's lawn tennis stars listed below in alphabetical order. See if your ratings of them match the computer. Award yourself one point each time your rating is the same.
Average score: 6 Greavsie: 7

1 Jimmy Connors
2 Jaroslav Drobny
3 Neale Fraser
4 Arthur Larsen
5 Rod Laver
6 Henri Leconte
7 John McEnroe
8 Manuel Orantes
9 Tony Roche
10 Mervyn Rose
11 Roscoe Tanner
12 Guillermo Vilas

ANSWERS

COMPUTER RATINGS, CRICKET (Page 179): 1. Len Hutton; 2. Barry Richards; 3. Sunil Gavaskar; 4. Bill Lawry; 5. Geoff Boycott; 6. Hanif Mohammad; 7. Gordon Greenidge; 8. John Edrich; 9. Glenn Turner; 10. Graham Gooch; 11. Bobby Simpson; 12. Chris Broad

Your Score

Running Total

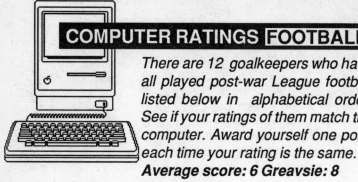

COMPUTER RATINGS FOOTBALL

There are 12 goalkeepers who have all played post-war League football listed below in alphabetical order. See if your ratings of them match the computer. Award yourself one point each time your rating is the same.
Average score: 6 Greavsie: 8

1 Gordon Banks
2 Peter Bonetti
3 Ray Clemence
4 Pat Jennings
5 Jack Kelsey
6 Peter Shilton
7 Neville Southall
8 Ron Springett
9 Frank Swift
10 Bert Trautmann
11 Bert Williams
12 Tommy Younger

ANSWERS

COMPUTER RATINGS, CRICKET (Page 180): 1. Jim Laker; 2. Sonny Ramadhin; 3. Richie Benaud; 4. Abdul Qadir; 5. Derek Underwood; 6. Lance Gibbs; 7. Bishen Bedi; 8. Tony Lock; 9. Hugh Tayfield; 10. Chandrasekhar; 11. Erapally Prasanna; 12. John Emburey.

97

There are four posers here about the rules of sport. What would YOU do if you were in charge? Four points for each correct judgment.
Average score: 8
Greavsie: 8

1. You are the umpire as the batsman hits a catchable ball back to the bowler. He is prevented from catching it because the non-striking batsman quite deliberately knocks it away with his bat. **Would you give the non-striking batsman out for obstruction?**

2. You are the referee as a goalkeeper takes a goal-kick with a gale-force wind blowing at his back. The ball sails down the pitch and goes first bounce into the net at the opposite end of the pitch without another player touching it. **Would you signal that a goal has been scored?**

3. You are the referee in a British title fight. Seconds before the bell at the end of the final round one of the boxers knocks his opponent flat on his back. You have just started to count when the bell goes to signal the end of the round. **Would you continue to count after the bell?**

4. You are called to give a ruling at the first tee in a golf match. One of the players has hooked his drive. The ball hit a tree and rebounded back to the tee and struck his opponent's golf bag that was being held by his caddie. **Would you rule that the drive should be taken again?**

ANSWERS

COMPUTER RATINGS (Page 181): 1. Rod Laver; 2. John McEnroe; 3. Jimmy Connors; 4. Jaroslav Drobny; 5. Neale Fraser; 6. Manuel Orantes; 7. Guillermo Villas; 8. Roscoe Tanner; 9. Mervyn Rose; 10. Henri Leconte; 11. Arthur Larsen; 12. Tony Roche.

Your Score

Running Total

Simply answer true or false to the following statements.
Two points for each correct answer.
Average score: 6 Greavsie: 8

98 TRUE OR FALSE?

1. World heavyweight champion Sonny Liston had 23 brothers and sisters.

2. Arnold Palmer was disqualified in the 1958 US Open for carrying one club too many.

3. Emil Zatopek was misrouted on his first marathon and won despite going 2 miles off course.

4. Graham Dilley was a Hatton Garden diamond setter until fired for taking time off to play cricket.

5. Actor Errol Flynn represented Australia's fencing team in the 1932 Los Angeles Olympics.

6. Arsenal Football Club once staged an archery tournament to raise money to pay off debts.

ANSWERS

COMPUTER RATINGS, FOOTBALL (Page 182): 1. Pat Jennings; 2. Peter Shilton; 3. Gordon Banks; 4. Frank Swift; 5. Jack Kelsey; 6. Ray Clemence; 7. Neville Southall; 8. Bert Trautmann; 9. Bert Williams; 10. Peter Bonetti; 11. Tommy Younger; 12. Ron Springett.

See how quickly you can identify a sports personality from the clues.
Average score: 4 Greavsie: 6

For 12 points: Our mystery guest was born in Oxford in 1961 and followed his Irish father into the sport in which he was to become famous.

For 10 points: He joined Frenchie Nicholson's stables at Cheltenham in 1977 and then teamed up with trainer Reg Hollinshead.

For 8 points: He had his first triumph on Paddy's Luck at Kempton Park in 1978 and in his first three years he rode 108 winners.

For 6 points: Trainer Michael Stoute snapped him up for his stable and he became the Aga Khan's top rider.

For 4 points: He won the 1981 Derby and the King George VI and Queen Elizabeth Stakes on board the ill-fated Shergar.

For 2 points: In 1983 he won the Irish Derby on Shareef Dancer and in the same year won the prestigious Washington International and the American Autumn Triple Crown on All Along.

ANSWERS

YOU BE THE JUDGE (Page 183): 1. No. The striking batsman would be given out for obstruction; 2. No. You cannot score direct from a goal-kick; 3. No. The final bell ends the contest even if a boxer is on the canvas; 4. No. The hole would automatically be awarded to the player who hooked the ball. The law states that 'if a player's ball be stopped or deflected by his opponent, his caddie or equipment, the opponent's side shall win the hole.'

Your Score

Running Total

A to Z

Your final test and there are 104 points at stake as we run through the alphabet on great champions, many of whom have featured on previous pages. Four points for each correct identification.

Average score: 60 Greavsie: 68

# of Champions

A is for the Olympic champion who was the first man to break the 13-minute barrier in the 5,000 metres.

B is for the batsman who averaged 115.66 for the season during Australia's tour of England in 1938.

C is for the Dutchman who was voted European Footballer of the Year three times during the 1970s.

D is for the snooker player from Plumstead who won the world championship for the first time in 1981.

E is for the Australian who won the Olympic 1500 metres gold medal in 1960 by the astonishing margin of 20 metres.

ANSWERS

Your Score

Running Total

TRUE OR FALSE (Page 184): 1. True; 2. False; 3. False; 4. True; 5. False; 6. True.

F is for the South American driver who became the youngest winner of the world motor racing title at 25.

G is for the three day event rider who won her sixth Badminton title on Beagle Bay in 1984.

H is for the footballer who scored an historic hat-trick for England at Wembley Stadium on July 30, 1966.

I is for the Heriots full back who scored 301 points for Scotland and the British Lions from 1973 to 1982.

J is for the former Llanelli full back who scored 1,245 goals in Rugby League matches for Leeds.

K is for the Russian gymnast who won gold medals for the beam and floor exercises in the 1972 Munich Olympics.

L is for the darts player who won £102,000 for scoring the first 501 with the minimum nine darts in a major event.

ANSWERS

GUESS THE GUEST (Page 185): The mystery personality is flat racing jockey Walter Swinburn.

M is for the world heavyweight champion who had 49 fights before retiring undefeated in 1956.

N is for the golfer who has won a record 20 major championships since joining the professional circuit in 1962.

O is for the American all-round athlete who won four Olympic gold medals in the Berlin Olympics.

P is for the jockey who rode his 28th and final classic winner on Commanche Run in the 1984 St Leger.

Q is for the Jamaican sprinter who won the 200 metres gold medal in the 1976 Montreal Olympics.

R is for the Irish road racer who won the 1987 Tour de France and confirmed his rating as No 1 cyclist in the world.

S is for the Cuban boxer who won three successive Olympic gold medals in the heavyweight division.

ANSWERS

T is for the first snooker player to score a maximum break of 147 in the World championships.

U is for the Kent left-arm spin bowler who took 297 wickets for England in 86 Test matches between 1966 and 1981.

V is for the 'Flying Finn' who won four gold medals on the track in the 1972 and 1976 Olympics.

W is for the American golfer who won the British Open for the first of five times at Carnoustie in 1975.

Y is for the Scottish international who was the first footballer to collect the FA Cup as captain of Liverpool.

Z is for the athlete who won the first of his four Olympic golds in the 10,000 metres in London in 1948.

? The final teaser: Which of the 25 stars featured in this quiz was born in Lancashire?

ANSWERS

A to Z OF CHAMPIONS (Page 187): Emerson FITTIPALDI; Lucinda GREEN; Geoff HURST; Andy IRVINE; Lewis JONES; Olga KORBUT; John LOWE.

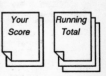

Your Score | Running Total

189

GREAVSIE'S SPORTS QUIZ CHALLENGE
HOW YOU RATE

Average score: 1,496 points
Greavsie's score: 1,808 points
Maximum score: 2,970 points

GREAVSIE'S GOLD
If you have scored more than 2,650 points you are without any question a Sports Mastermind. A gold medal performance. Greavsie bows the knee to you.

GREAVSIE'S SILVER
If you have scored between 2,200 and 2,650 points you have an impressive all-round grasp of sport. A silver medal performance. Greavsie's looking green!

GREAVSIE'S BRONZE
If you have scored between 1808 and 2,200 points you have given Greavsie a beating and you take the bronze in this challenge match. Congratulations.

ANSWERS

A to Z OF CHAMPIONS (Page 188): Rocky MARCIANO; Jack NICKLAUS; Jesse OWENS; Lester PIGGOTT; Don QUARRIE; Stephen ROCHE; Teofilo STEVENSON.

1500 PLUS POINTS

If you have scored more than 1,500 points but less than 1,808 you have just failed to beat Greavsie. But you mounted an excellent challenge and have a much better-than-average knowledge of sports facts and figures.

1000 PLUS POINTS

If you have scored between 1,000 and 1,500 points, you have given Greavsie a good match but have had to give second best to the Old Groaner. You can claim an average all-round sports knowledge.

750 PLUS POINTS

If you have scored between 750 and 1,000 points that's just below average and you have got to concede defeat to Greavsie. You have got quite a lot of record book swatting to do before the next challenge!

LESS THAN 750

If you have scored less than 750 points, Greavsie has really scored against you. Anyway, thank you for accepting the Sports Quiz Challenge. We hope that playing the game has given you a lot of entertainment and also a little enlightenment.

ANSWERS

A to Z OF CHAMPIONS (Page 189): Cliff THORBURN; Derek UNDER-WOOD; Lasse VIREN; Tom WATSON; Ron YEATS; Emil ZATOPEK. Final Teaser: Geoff Hurst, who was born at Ashton-under-Lyme, Lancashire.

HOW WELL D'YOU KNOW...?
JIMMY GREAVES

Here's a final test that Greavsie didn't take. How well d'you know the man who was arguably the greatest goalscorer of them all? You must get five or more right to prove you know Greavsie well. The answers are below.

1. Where in London was he born in the year 1940?

2. How old was he when he made his First Division debut?

3. With which club did he start his professional football career?

4. Which former England international centre-forward was his first manager?

5. To which Italian club was he transferred in 1960?

6. What was the unusual fee that Tottenham paid to bring him home from Italy?

7. He scored more First Division goals than any other player in history—287, 317, or 357?

8. Against which club did he score an FA Cup Final goal in just 180 seconds?

9. How many goals did he score in his 57 appearances for England—36, 40 or 44?

10. With which club did he finish his Football League playing career?

ANSWERS

HOW WELL D'YOU KNOW JIMMY GREAVES?: 1. East Ham; 2. 17-years-old; 3. Chelsea; 4. Ted Drake; 5. AC Milan; 6. £99,999 (Spurs manager Bill Nicholson did not want to weigh him down with the pressure of being the first £100,000 footballer); 7. 357; 8. Burnley (in the 1962 Final); 9. 44 (only Bobby Charlton—49 in 106 games—has scored more); 10. West Ham United.

192